D1548147

SHADOWING DIZZY GILLESPIE
100th BIRTHDAY ANNIVERSARY
By David G. Brown

Brave Down Books

Brave Down Books
7302 Huntsmen Circle 16-D
Anchorage AK 99518

Printed in the United States

Library of Congress Control Number: 2017951387
ISBN 978-0-9854429-3-4

www.BraveDownBooks.com

Dedicated to my sons,
Adam Wolf and Luke Elijah Brown

Table of Contents

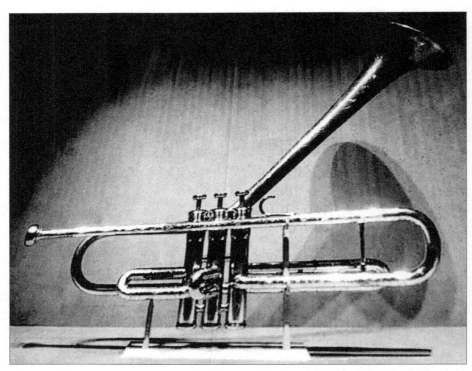

Photo courtesy of the Charles Lake Collection.

A Few Words from the Author

I was conducting a final edit of *Return of the Free Faller,* a character-driven historical novel revolving around the lives of two troubled friends from New England. That's the novel. The historical part of *Free Faller* is all about Dizzy Gillespie.

It was Ron Della Chiesa who suggested I condense the book. Once I told him the Dizzy part was between 75 and 100 pages, he felt it was the perfect size for a novella. I took Ron's advice, extracted all the Dizzy material, made the necessary edits, added loads of Gillespian photos, and, lastly, produced the book you are holding in your hand.

What makes *Shadowing Dizzy Gillespie* unusual is our unexpected convergence. I met Dizzy in February of 1985. At that time he was 68 years old and I was 44. I was a music-loving businessman from Woonsocket, RI. Mr. Gillespie was a music-loving, famous bon voyant from Cheraw, SC. We were different generations, religions, races, and upbringings. We were worlds apart. It would seem improbable that I'd be writing a novella about him. But here we are, celebrating the 100th anniversary of his birth. Just that thought alone gives me goosebumps.

The most difficult task in writing about John Birks "Dizzy" Gillespie is writing the way he talks. His tone is singular with a style that, in itself, is unique. For example, in virtually all of John's conversations, I heard that wonderfully deep, husky voice, most times starting a sentence with, "I, I, I, uh (pause), I, I, I..." He said "dat" instead of "that" and annihilated the rest of the King's English, while at the same time creating his own verbiage: Dizzyisms.

I sucked it all in, loving that voice, rejoicing in his thought-out postulations, humor, optimism, his mellowness, intonations and intent.

To write like Dizzy talks, I think, would be unfair to the reader. That's the rub. I will not put that task upon you. Instead, hear him as you read, knowing he's talking like dat, and stuttering like diss, with a bunch of "I's" thrown in for good measure. Actually, the more I thought about his stuttering sounds, I came to the conclusion they were errors of commission, maybe a subconscious tactic, giving him a reprieve, a few extra moments to collect his thoughts and carry on as best he could. After all, John was a bebopper, the king of bebop; his mind worked so fast, those stuttering "I's" were really like notes preceding his words.

Please take note that all the dialogue is not 100% verbatim. Close, by all means, and always expressing the intent of the speaker(s). You'll also see that I rarely give dates. For me it ain't all that important. Life was timeless in the company of the maestro. Each time with him had a life of its own.

Having been a shadow, my mission is to animate

Dizzy, bring him into your reading room as if he were extending those cheeks on *The Muppet Show*. I hope you can sense his very essence. So, let's give it a go. Let's bebop.

" Cheek to Cheek "

Photo courtesy of the Charles Lake Collection.

The Maestro

"I'm driving down to Washington," Rene Berard tells me. "Late tomorrow night. I have an interview with one of the execs from Tennis International." Rene is calling from Providence, and I'm home in Woonsocket. "These people are providing me with five-star accommodations including a suite at the Dupont Plaza. Now understand, this will be about a one-hour interview. The rest of the time we can party in our nation's capital. Wanna go?"

When we hit the D.C. Beltway at sunrise, Rene bought a *Washington Post* and announced that we were going to a joint called Blues Alley in Georgetown. "Dizzy Gillespie is playing, and I voted Dizzy for President."

Me, I was up for anything. But not as juiced as Rene about seeing Dizzy. I had a flashback to my high school years, my introductory era to jazz. A buddy of mine, Stevie Max, whom I went to my first Newport Jazz Festival with in 1958, told me Dizzy was a clown. "Joking around was more important to him than playing," Stevie said. And for years that left an impression on me.

This was late February in 1985 and it was 80 degrees in Washington.

Turns out the real heat that night would be coming from the stage at Blues Alley.

We had a great table, close up and in the center of the room. As soon as the spotlight illuminated Dizzy on stage, he announced, "GILLESPIE'S MY NAME AND MUSIC IS MY GAME."

He then raised his shiny gold, magical trumpet to the roof, those Gillespian cheeks filled with air, his lips disappeared into the mouthpiece, and he jumped right into "Manteca." The groove was tight, loud, and straight-ahead bebop jazz, a genre he invented with alto great Charlie Parker. I was captivated and captured – hook, line and sinker. This was the best, the maestro with game face on, all business. The clowning part of his performance was strictly show-biz schtick. I wanted to stick a voodoo needle into Stevie Max.

At the conclusion of the first set, Rene tapped me on the shoulder. I knew he'd brought a few recreational drugs along. Rene's a tennis pro, and was all about recreation. He wanted me to take a walk with him to the men's room so I could "cover the door" while he did what he had to do.

When we entered the lav located on the second floor, Rene locked himself inside the cubicle. Much to my surprise, standing at a commode was Dizzy Gillespie, the grand maestro himself, taking a hearty whiz. We were the only people in the room. I was awe-stricken. Oddly, I saw him make a strange, twitching full-body movement. Then the trumpet man, like some outraged Brahma bull, released a blast of gas that nearly knocked me across the room. Oh my. It was explosive.

I couldn't restrain myself. "Well Mr. Gillespie, now I've heard you play from your better set of cheeks!"

He bounced up and down, still squirting away, missing the bowl, and laughing his ass off.

"I like dat, I like dat one." He spoke in a heavy-deep drawl, "You're a baaad muther f--ker, muther f--ker." He zipped up, made sure everything was in place, and said, "C'mon, take a walk with me."

What? He's asking me to take a walk with him?

I followed, not getting too close in case of a sneak attack.

His dressing room was small, but filled with people. He offered me a drink, which I graciously accepted, and he explained to his friends how we just met. "Best set of cheeks; sheeet, that's the best one-liner I've heard this year." He sat down at a table and started playing cards with a heavyset accountant from Cleveland, and continued talking to me.

Then, without any prompting, Mr. Gillespie started giving an oration about the blues.

"I can guarantee ya one thing. The blues, in it's truest sense, brings the greatest pain of all. I'm talkin about when your chick has up and left ya, and ya didn't want her to leave. Jilted is what I'm talkin about. That's feelin the blues. Nothin like it, ya hear. Worse than havin a loved one buy the farm. Shit, them folks are dead and gone. When your chick is out there bangin some other cat, while you're home layin on the sofa guzzling Jack, eatin your heart and soul out, plottin, feelin endless aches of the heart, that's the blues all right. Badness, ya know. Listen to Pops, Billy, Ella, Etta James, and BB the King. They sing it like it is. They knows bout the blues, baby. Me too. See what I'm sayin?"

We spent a good half hour asking questions and sharing information, as though we were supposed to, if that made any sense. It was so easy and natural being with him; like family. We talked about my home state of Rhode Island, how he enjoyed performing at the annual Jazz Festival. "Newport ain't no smoke-filled, jazzy city room. It's big and open, like playin in Yankee Stadium. Over 10,000 folks come from all over to pay respect. And, ya know, I don't live that far away, in Englewood, NJ."

As we all headed downstairs for the second set, he stopped and said, "That was fun. You blew me away with, 'my better set of cheeks.' Here's a little memento from me to you. It'll bring you good luck." He handed me a small shiny lapel pin. "If you ever run into 'the Whale' up there in New England, show it to him."

"The Whale?"

"Uh huh. Charley 'The Whale' Lake Keljakian. Keljakian means lake in Armenian. He's my business manager and he's from Revere Beach in Massachusetts."

"I know Revere Beach. That's where the Wonderland

dog track is."

"And that's where you'll find the Whale. He calls me Birks."

"OK. Thanks for the pin, Dizzy. I feel very privileged. Hey, I got a question?"

"What's that?"

"Can I call you John?"

"Hell yeah, you can call me anytime. Actually John is my given name. I like dat."

"Good, so do I, cuz I don't think you're very dizzy, Dizzy."

"Thanks, David. Hey, you made my night. Enjoy the second set. It's usually the best."

As we parted company, he said to me, "Ya know, the best cymbals, Zildjian, are made in Armenia."

"Is that why you hired the Whale?"

"Huh, never thought of it that way before." John pointed his finger at me. "Naw, the Whale's my main man. He a baad muther f--ker, just like you."

When I got back to the table, Rene was all wired up, in a major tizzy, eyes all red and blurry, and his nose dripping. "Where you been, amigo? I looked all over for you, thought you were dead, or shanghaied, or somethin. Did you hear that fart?"

What could I tell him? Throughout the night, I kept looking at John's pin. It was circular with a trumpet in the middle, the bell turned up. John's calling card. On the back it read, "Made in France." Throughout the night I took loads of notes.

Photo by author.

"YOU'RE IN!"

It was difficult getting back into my normal routine upon returning home. I was still affected by the great weekend in D.C., the warm weather, the music, and of course the chance to meet Dizzy – I mean John.

Now this is where the plot becomes curious and coincidental. Midweek I get a call from John Chan asking if I'd be interested in joining him for a drive to Boston. "There's a birthday bash at the Copley Plaza for Ron Della Chiesa, you know, the host of the popular WGBH weekly radio program, *Music America.*"

John Chan is the second-generation owner of Chan's Fine Oriental Dining, a Woonsocket Chinese restaurant that his father opened in the mid 1900s. During the past few years, John's been holding musical events at the restaurant, mostly jazz, and developed a friendship with Della Chiesa. Who was I to refuse such a tempting invitation? Been listening to *Music America* for years. Great radio.

Copley Square ain't square. On the contrary, it's ultracool. A tract of land set smack dab in the middle of downtown Boston, the Back Bay section, is where folks from the Mayflower wandered about, and where plans for the American Revolutionary War took place. It is one of our first national landmarks. As is the Copley Plaza, a gray brick and ornate seven-story international hotel of consequence. The place just oozes history. It's where Boston Blue Bloods and the elite meet to eat. Perpendicular to the Copley is the Boston Public Library, another early American monument, which was domicile to scores of ghostly Massachusetts authors, poets, and creative writing professors. Think Poe.

What a Square. There is a natural mystic aura of energy and spirit flowing through the air here – generations' worth.

I had been to the Copley on several occasions, on weekdays, where Dave McKenna, a fellow Woonsocket native and Concord Jazz label pianist, entertained. Dave played on the first floor in the elegant Plaza Bar that had beautiful chandeliers. He would sit at his Steinway in the middle of the room, with music lovers perched on stools. He played requests. He'd turn each tune into magic. His left hand was often called a rhythm section. David McKenna, may his soul rest in peace, had the head of a bald eagle. His face should have been chiseled on New Hampshire's "Old Man of the Mountain."

Took us forever to park the car; Boston, what else is new? Circled the block a few times and finally found a spot in front of the Cafe Budapest, also where the elite meet to eat. A moist, icy wind blew in from the harbor, creating a typical Boston February night. Felt good to finally arrive at the Copley Plaza lobby.

The party was held in that same chandelier room, and it wasn't hard spotting Ron Della Chiesa because everyone was surrounding him. When the crowd settled down, John Chan introduced me to Ron. At first blush I felt out of place, thinking, really, what the hell am I doing here? A hayseed from Rhode Island with no musical skills other than a good ear.

Della Chiesa was all smiles. What the hell; it was his birthday and half of Boston was there. We shook hands and, in turn, Ron introduced us to, of all people, Charley "The Whale" Lake Keljakian, Dizzy's manager. That took me by surprise. Actually, Mr. Lake Keljakian seemed to be a bit disinterested, off somewhere else, so to speak.

Until I handed him John's pin. "Ya know, Mr. Lake, this truly is a strange coincidence," I said. "Last weekend I was at a club called Blues Alley in Georgetown and I met Dizzy Gillespie."

Mr. Lake frowned and pointed his finger at me. "You're the guy in the shitter."

"That'd be me. The guy in the shitter." His face lit up. I showed him the trumpet pin.

"I'll tell you right now, not many people get that pin," Charley The Whale said. "They only did fifty of em. Made in Paris, ya know."

"Should I give it back to you?"

"Hell no. It's yours. Treasure it." He tapped me on the shoulder as though we were teammates, and he was captain. "I swear to God, Birks has not stopped talking about last week at Blues Alley. He calls it 'The Toilet Affair.'" He smiled. "I feel like I already know you. Birks said you got him laughin so hard, he pissed on his shoes."

"As a witness, I can attest to that. But it was his gas explosion that sparked the occasion. Thank god no one lit a match." We both laughed. "He told me you call him Birks."

"That's right; Birks it is. We've been together a long time, you know." Charley The Whale was about the same size as John, a tinch shorter with black graying hair. And casually dressed for a Copley Plaza event – no tie, wearing a black sports jacket. If Dorothy Kilgallen was playing *What's My Line?*, she'd immediately guess Charley was Dizzy Gillespie's manager.

"I like Birks better than Dizzy," I told the Whale. "Actually, I asked if it was OK to call him John, and he approved."

"He probably would have preferred mother f--ker. One thing for sure, and I guess you found this out, he ain't very dizzy."

Neither was Charley.

"I was just amazed at John's versatility," I said. "He owned the audience within a minute. I can honestly say last Saturday night was one of the best times of my life."

"He has that affect on everyone, swear to god. And he truly took to you, no word of a lie. So, whether you like it or not, you're in."

"I am? What the hell does that mean?"

"Whenever you can come and be with us, there

will always be a pass waiting for you at the ticket office or will call window. Whenever or wherever you wanna attend, call either Birks or myself and we'll handle everything."

"Holy shit. Are you kidding me, or what?"

"Dead serious. When he makes up his mind, that's it. So welcome on board."

"I'll be damned. Ain't this a how-do-you-do. I feel like I just won a lottery." I shook hands with the Whale again. "Ya know something, Mr. Keljakian?"

"What's that?"

"You're a bad muther f--ker. That's what you are."

"You got that right, and don't forget it. Now, for openers, in three weeks Mr. Birks is playin at the Boston Opera House with his United Nations Orchestra. I'm psyched about that one. For that gig, I'll have you hang out with me backstage, introduce you to a few of his crew members, and you'll get a kick out of the party afterwards."

"Opera House? Party?"

"Yeh. The famed Boston Opera House. There's usually some kind of post performance action. Never know who's bound to show up."

"Damn. Let me ask a silly question?"

"Shoot."

"Think any of these people would be interested in smoking some ganja?"

"Why? Are you a cop or somethin?"

"Oh no. No, no, not at all. I've got a friend from

Jamaica who keeps me supplied with some high-octane ganja."

"You're going to make Mr. Birks very happy. Just keep in mind on gig days he does not indulge till after business is done. Wait till I clue him in on this."

"Well, let's see what happens after the Opera House."

"Here's my card. Call me a few days prior to the gig and I'll have everything ready for you. At times, if you want, you can even bring a friend along."

"Consider it done. Charley, I am so damn excited about this. Thank you so much."

Ron Della Chiesa wandered back. He was feeling no pain. Lipstick was smeared on his cheek. He said, "Not many people know this but both Charley and I are trumpet players, not exactly all-stars, I must say, and erstwhile at this point in time. But back in the day, we could play – until we started listening to the likes of Dizzy." He paused contemplatively. "You know, that craving and love to play propelled us forward. And that's one of the main reasons Charley and I are both involved in music to this day."

Photo by author.
The Whales' 65th surprise birthday party at The El Morocco in Worcester, MA. That's his mom.

Photo by author.
What a bash. Ron Della Chiesa hosted. That's my bro Greg Abate on tenor and Dick Johnson leading the Artie Shaw Orchestra late into the night. Gillespie vibes were everywhere.

The Three Whalers

Photo courtesy of the Charles Lake Collection.

The Boston Opera House

I just cannot get over it. Spoke with Charley The Whale who gave me instructions and directions to the Boston Opera House. My guess is that he's conditioned, after so many years, to following up on accommodations and requests from Dizzy lovers all over the world. "You're gonna take 95 to 93 and get onto Mass Ave, right?"

"Charley, I've already got the directions, thank you."

"Good, good. When you get to the door, use the valet service. Just give him your keys and he'll handle your car. Nothin to worry about, see."

Prior to heading off to the Boston Opera House, I did some research on John and his hometown of Cheraw, SC, in Chesterfield County, the home of the Cheraw and Pee Dee Indians. It's an historic place, noted for Confederate aristocracy, and unwillingly hosted the Union's General William T. Sherman during the Civil War. One of the early English settlers was a James Gillespie, who started a trading center and water mill around 1740. Almost from the beginning, African Americans were brought there as slaves. Holy shit, could I ever dare to discuss this with John?

The Boston Opera House, located at 539 Washington Street, is in a tough section of Beantown. Just as the Whale said, my pass was at the will call window and I was directed to a door leading back stage. We were about an hour prior to curtain call and it was busy. The first person I saw was Ignacio Berroa, Dizzy's drummer from his quintet. And next to him was percussionist Tito Puente. They were assembling their drum sets, laughing and talking in Spanish.

I felt a slap on my shoulder. "Hey, you made it." It was the Whale. "Wanna help out?"

"Sure. Of course."

"Good. Take this box of CDs out to the lobby. You'll see Ginny; that's my chick. She'll be setting up a table to sell these things. Grab one for yourself. Then come on back stage and I'll show you around."

Ginny Cook, coincidentally, also lives in Woonsocket, so we had plenty to talk about. She used to be a Broadway and Vegas dancer. And met the Whale "along the way." Along the way. I liked that. Sounded like a line in a movie – romantic and mysterious.

I told her how amazed I was to be there. She laughed. "Stay around long enough and Dizz will figure out a way to get you involved."

"Involved?"

"Yes, involved. I can't explain it. But it seems most everyone in his circle is involved. You'll see what I mean. It's a good thing." She smiled. "Maybe you'll play an instrument."

"Don't humor me, Ginny; I can't play shit. I'd screw up a triangle."

"Who the hell knows. Just have a good time. If Dizz

is happy to have you around, that's all that matters. He surrounds himself with quite a crew of talented upbeat cats. And, if you've never seen his United Nations Group, you are in for a treat; that's a guarantee."

"Thanks, Ginny."

As Charley "The Whale" Lake led me to Dizzy's dressing room, there was controlled chaos taking place on the stage, which was set behind a curtain that had to rise 50 feet to the ceiling. All kinds of action, last minute preparations, as roadies set up music stands, tapped and checked mikes, placed a beverage by a chair. I spotted the great saxophonist James Moody warming up.

The Whale said, "Next time, you'll have to get here for the sound check. At times it's almost as interesting as the actual gig."

I took a deep breath upon entering the maestro's dressing room. The setting felt old and historical, with a sniff of musty fragrance. I laughed as soon as I saw him, part in awe of the moment, and recalling the vision of him cutting that introductory fart.

"Hello, David," he said, giving me a big hug. I almost melted.

"Hello, John."

"You made it. I'm glad." He clapped his hands. "Gonna do my best not to pee on my shoes tonight." Everyone cracked up. "David, this here is Arturo Sandoval. He's a longtime friend from the great cigar-smokin island of Cuba. When it comes to playin the horn, he can teach me a thing or two." Arturo flashed a shy smile. "Yes sah, Arturo here, he's about as bad as bad can be. You'll find that out tonight."

John played a significant role in helping Arturo migrate to the United States. Very dramatic set of circumstances; they even made a movie about Arturo's odyssey: *For Love of Country*. John loves Cuba for its beauty and especially all the great musical talent. Hell, he brought Cubano/Latin rhythms to American jazz. In 1989 he did an avant garde film called *A Night in Havana*. There's a shot of him smoking a cigar with Fidel, which caused some smack from the American media.

I liked the way John's dressing room was set up. A table with appetizers and a bucket with an assortment of beverages. John sipped away on an iced tea. He sat at a desk covered with gifts, memorabilia, and a sheet of paper with the songs to be played. There was a big wall mirror, and a clothes rack with a beautifully designed African robe, neatly pressed, on a hanger. On the floor by his side was an unimposing black case, the domicile of John's livelihood, half open and displaying his trumpet, the bell pointed up.

He asked me to hand it to him, which I did with reverence. "Grab a drink, sit back, and enjoy." He blew into it silently. Muffler cleared, both Arturo and Dizzy turned their keys to start their engines, and proceeded through a series of exercises. The speed of their playing was incredibly in sync. They chatted and nodded to each other. Both Whale and I sat in awe.

A knock on the door and in walked Flora Purim with her husband, Airto Moreira, and Claudio Roditi, all from Brazil. Flora said, "How am I suppose to sing to that?"

Dizzy wrapped his arms around her and said, "Hey woman, thought you weren't gonna make it."

Airto replied, "We would have walked if we had to."

Flora was as large in life as Dizzy. She'd been singing with his big band since 1980. She'd performed with all the greats. What added jump to her character was the fact that in 1974 she was busted on a cocaine rap, and served hard time for over a year.

"Are y'all ready?" Dizz asked.

"Absolutely," Claudio confirmed.

"Good, cuz we hit in ten minutes."

The Whale brought me over to a spot behind the curtain, aside the stage. I looked out to a capacity crowd. "My god," I said. "This place is jammin. How many people do you think are here?"

The Whale replied without hesitation, "Two thousand six hundred and seventy-seven. Beautiful joint, ain't it?"

I absorbed the magnificence of it all. The aura, the action behind the curtain and the buzz on the other side: an audience in anticipation as if awaiting the sun to break above the horizon at dawn's early light. For some macabre reason I suddenly visualized Mary

Todd and Abraham Lincoln sitting in the balcony.

"Yes, Charley, this place is gorgeous. And to think John is so popular that he could be invited to play in a room meant for symphonies and the opera."

"Yes. All true." Charley The Whale flashed a look at me and said, "Here we go."

The curtain rose and the quintet (John Lee on bass guitar; Sam Rivers on tenor and soprano; Ignacio Barroa, drummer; and Ed Cherry, guitar) got the action underway. I remember thinking back to Blues Alley, that first night, how I found it curious John didn't use a piano and stand-up bass; made me think of Bob Dylan fusing folk music with rock. These were the same artists I saw in Georgetown and they warmed up the room, perfectly, each taking solo turns. They played for about five minutes.

Then John walked right by me, could feel the heat from his body, and got a sniff of after shave. He gave me a pat on the back, and hit the stage wearing that sheiky African long robe and a linen African hat, shoes spit-shined. The place went nuts and he hadn't even struck a note.

Heaven, I was in f--king heaven, in an opera house, along with 2,677 adoring jazz fans.

Tito Puente, Puerto Rico's most acclaimed musician, walked by me and onto the stage. He was talking to himself, raising his arms with drumsticks in hand, and flashing a huge smile. Then came Cuba's pride and joy, Arturo Sandoval, along with Claudio Roditi.

Arturo, Claudio and Dizzy would act as a trio of trumpets among an orchestra of jazz giants. Whale said, "They're like Mays, Clemente and Junior Griffey. Know what I mean?"

Dizzy pulled the microphone out of the stand, and blew into it – his first note of the evening. "Ladies and gentlemen, I'd like to introduce the band." And they began shaking hands with each other, making jokes, slappin fives, shadow boxing.

The Whale elbowed me. "Check this out." Dizzy was bowing to Flora Purim as she came on stage; then he sauntered over and lovingly wrapped his arms around her. At that point Airto hustled out and pointed at Dizz. "Hey, don't be messin with my old lady!"

The two great saxophonists, Paquito D'Rivera and Charles Moody, joined in along with pianist Danilo Perez. Lastly, Dizzy introduced his quintet; and, without hesitation, the master musicians went to work. I looked up at the ceiling giving thanks, just knowing the music gods were keeping watch.

Dizzy introduced each song with a soft, clear, husky voice. His words and timing were precise and professional. He bopped into his own brand of humor, using Charles Moody as his straight man.

Late in the performance, Dizzy called Mario Bauzá to the stage. Bauzá was in his late seventies, a renowned trumpeter, and the founding father of Latin jazz. "This here is the main man. Deep in my heart,

Cuba is my first love, and that's where Mario is from."

Arturo piped in, "Me too."

Mario Bauzá was like Dizzy's musical brother and muse combined. He told us, "It's Mario who helped me bring Cuban and Latin rhythms into American jazz. Our friendship began when we both played in the Cab Calloway Band."

I could picture the two of them messing around on stage back in the 40s, while the Calloway rhythm section was playing. Or when ole Cal was singing hi-de-ho hoochie coochie songs. Cab would peek over and see Dizzy playing games, making faces, and it would piss him off. The Gillespie stabbing of Cab Calloway remains one of America's greatest jazz anecdotes, with all kinds of cockamamie variations.

The Whale whispered to me, "That's some shit."

It's impossible, in words, to fully explain and describe what I heard during those two hours. It incorporated the audio senses, the flow, teamwork, an orderliness, playing *tight,* as jazz folk will say. There was a plethora of singular personality and voice presented through each artist's instrument.

One thing became very clear to me: Dizzy Gillespie runs the show; a perfectionist, a taskmaster presenting virtuoso performances every time, and expecting the same from his fellow musicians.

Once the curtain fell, Dizzy headed for his dressing room to cool off.

The Whale said, "C'mon, let's take a walk to the

lobby. My son, Paul, is selling CDs. We'll give him a hand. Birks will come down to sign stuff in a few; then we'll go upstairs."

"Upstairs?" I figured I'd be looking for the valet in a few minutes.

"Yeah, upstairs there's a party goin on. The fun has just begun."

For close to an hour, John talked with admirers and signed everything from 33$\frac{1}{3}$ vinyls and CDs to t-shirts and baseball hats. There was a pile of gifts on the table including signed books and CDs, a camera, a pair of sun glasses, cookies, and flowers. Once we got upstairs, Dizzy and the Whale were engulfed by a hoard of enthusiastic Bostonians.

Grabbed a glass of chardonnay off a tray, along with a plateful of shrimp, cocktail sauce and a squeeze of lemon. Next to me was a lovely young nurse from Puerto Rico. Fine looking lady, very smart and witty. This could have been interesting till Mario Bauzá walked over. The nurse was his wife, and he abruptly whisked her away.

John was deep in conversation with a middle-aged couple. I was curious and got close enough to hear him delivering his personal recipe for harmony grits, line item by line item, animated about every detail. "Ya don't wanna get the heat too fired up..." He gestured for me to come over, and introduced me to a former neighbor from Cheraw. She, in turn, introduced me to her husband, who was a mathematics professor at

Harvard, and a Nobel Peace Prize recipient.

Before heading home, I shook hands with Charley and thanked him for taking such good care of me. Then I spotted John, standing in a corner by himself, taking a momentary respite. I walked over. "John, what's going through your head right now?"

"Just reminding myself how important it is to always leave them wanting more."

And to think, all of this emerged from the gaseous confines of the men's room at Blues Alley. Now I'm hob-nobbing with Nobel Peace Prize winners.

Photo by author.

Puerto Rico's favorite drummer, Tito Puente.

Waterville Valley, NH

The Whale was telling me over the phone, "We're heading up to Waterville Valley next weekend. It's a big ski resort. They've got a month-long series of music. This weekend is Dave Brubeck with his son Chris, and then Birks follows with the Quintet. I figure that's about a three hour and forty-five minute drive from your digs. I-95 north, hook up to 93, straight shot to Lincoln, NH, and bingo. Nice country, White Mountains, the Old Man of the Mountain, mountains everywhere. You wanna come?"

Charley was spot on as far as the distance and drive. Arrived at the Waterville Valley Resort, followed directions to my assigned condo, dropped off my bags, which included a dozen Jamaican spliffs – a bobbon bonus for the gala and vicissitudes of late night pleasures.

I headed over to the Resort Conference Center. The New Hampshire air smelled fresher than back home in inland Rhode Island, where textile mills built during the industrial revolution left decades of molecular waste. Here it felt more in unison with Mother, amongst the fragrances of pines and white birch, and everything pristine that comes from fresh water lakes and streams. A comfortable setting for pristine music.

The quintet was in the midst of a sound check.

Dizzy, standing behind a music stand, was playing a Jew's harp, also known as a jaw or mouth harp. The volume on the sound system was turned way up, sending a twanging vibration throughout the room. He was mouthing and working the bejeezus out of that little thing. It was evident the maestro was totally comfortable and in command during sound check. This was his element, his world where creativity and hard work ruled his life.

Charley, off to the side, was opening a box of CDs and setting up a table for evening sales. Dizzy spotted me with a smile and a thumbs up.

I was immediately caught up in everything music: The sound tech moved knobs up and down, while John Lee adjusted his guitar to it. Sam Rivers was talking to himself. Ignacio Barroa was tightening up his drum set, a smile glued to his face. On the other hand, Ed Cherry, a big, bald, serious-looking dude standing in the back left of the five, was mulling over a guitar string. Dizzy sat down at the piano – I mean "the piana" – and explaining something to John Lee.

Oh yes, I liked this. I could hear everyone on the stage and what they were saying and doing. Could hear their footsteps. And just watching John from close range, so comfortable and happy, so incredibly tuned in, made me equally as happy. It was like being at a Broadway play, watching great thespians, only it wasn't acting, it was the real thing. Like the Whale said, "Sound check can be as interesting as the show."

I'm mulling over the possibility that, during a past incarnation, I must have been involved in music. I do know my senses fire up with music. I become so attuned, enrapt whenever I'm in that environment. Being close to a Dizzy Gillespie production was, for me, what it must have been like for the Apostles hanging out with Jesus.

Instead of standing alongside the stage, I sat at a table with Charley and Ginny. The program was very similar to Blues Alley, only this time, Dizzy played around with that Jew's harp. He walked on stage wearing plaid slacks, a thick wool sweater and a Mets baseball hat. He held his horn upright, pulled the mike to his mouth and announced, "Gillespie's my name, and music's my game."

The ski crowd loved him. He left them wanting more.

An hour after the gig, we were back in the condo. The band members stopped in and I brought forth my ganja gifts, the Healing of the Nations.

John began talking about his days in high school. "My public school teachers in Cheraw believed I had some musical talent. I figure my father had something to do with that too, cuz he was all about music. So they managed to get me into Laurinburg Institute. I was 16 years old. This famous black southern man came up with the idea to begin the Laurinburg school for Afro-American blacks in the early 1900s. Ever hear of Booker T. Washington? That's no bullshit, man." John bobbed his head up and down. "Ha, I was institutionalized. Can you imagine dat; I went to good ole Booker T's school. Booker knew what was happenin.

"Didn't stay very long cuz my family moved and I went with em. Then, not long after that, we moved to Philly for a while. One of the few things that stands out about Laurinburg is how cool it was to put on a football uniform. It was baaaad. For about a month of my life, I was a bad-ass football player. Booker's school is in North Carolina." He pointed at me. "Hey, you're from the Boston area. Remember Sam Jones? He played for the Boston Celtics? Well Sambo, he went to Laurenburg too."

"I do remember Sam Jones. From the Bill Russell era. He was a great guard. KC Jones and Sam Jones – no relation – lit up the Boston Garden."

"You got that right. And Laurinburg Institute is where my man, Sam-man, went. Uh huh."

I commented, "That's some serious education…"

"Hell yeah – an excellent school. But the truth is, I'm a graduate of the school of hard knocks, baby. Let me tell ya – back then, my hometown wasn't exactly throwin pajama parties for the likes of me. Get what I'm sayin?" John paused and tugged on the short mass of hair below his lower lip. "I'm thinkin back to a gig we played many years ago. Many, many years ago – like a lifetime ago. Charlie Parker was with me. This was in a ballroom down south somewhere.

I think in Georgia. Max Roach was there and he gets a kick out of tellin the story, not cuz a me, mind you, but because of Charlie and his advanced intellect, his ar tic u late ness." John laughed. "Lateness was a Charlie Parker trademark."

He continued, "As a matter of fact, Max relates the story on a recent album [MAX + DIZZY, A&M CD 6404] we produced in France. What happens is, it's after the gig and I headed straight for the men's room, a room I ain't suppose to be occupyin, see." John laughed at his words. "Damn, this good ole fella and me, why we'd be talkin back and forth only a few minutes earlier. Now, the mutha f--ka comes up from behind and whacks me on the head with a coke bottle – not a can but a glass bottle – and blindsides me, he did. I runs a hand along the back of my head. Shit, there's blood everywhere.

"Then good ole Charlie Parker comes over and says, 'You hit my friend, you cur.'

"Still not so sure why Max loves to tell that story. That was a baad night." He ran his hand through his hair. "School of hard knocks, I'm telling ya."

I nodded.

John paused and asked, "Hey, David, I'm curious. Do you play any instruments?"

"Yeah, my ear," I replied. "I do believe I'm a five star listener. I can feel sound. But, when it comes to playing, anything..." My eyes dropped. "I am awful, talentless, lacking in the ability to coordinate both hands and fingers. My buddy Greg Abate tried to teach me the tenor sax. First thing I did was drop it. I swear the birds outside the window were wincing when I finally brought forth some sound, just awful … but we sure did laugh … and I sure do love to listen."

"I know you do."

"I'll tell you this. I've been writing all my life. I love to write, swear to god, and I know some day I'll be published."

"You sound pretty convincing. Ya really mean that?"

"Hey John, I love to write." It was the first time I felt a little awkward, maybe out of place. Then again, I felt good that, in some way, he was working me.

John changed the subject. He stood. "That's a Miles tune playing in the background." He pointed at the CD player and said, "I'll teach you something. Listen to that. Miles is blowin horn and Kenny Garrett is on sax. See how they're going back and forth; that's *call and return*. Some say call and response." He stopped the player. "There, right there, a perfect example. It's a beautiful thing, as old as the hills of Africa. The drums of Africa. Remember, the drums are the first instrument and it served a purpose of call and return from village to village, like smoke signals, ya know. Miles and Kenny are emulating that through trumpet and saxophone."

After the band members left, John sat back and seemed to relax more, as though he was done with work. Fact is, he led those guys, and he treated each musician like an employee and brother. Each gig, he wanted them thinking like they were taking the playing field for a World Series game. His four accomplices practiced diligently and John fully expected a five star performance … every gig out. That involved dedication to the art form, a love and respect for the music.

John's cell phone rang. He got into an entangled conversation with his wife, Lorraine. Could hear her high-pitched voice. She was calling from their home in Englewood, NJ, very upset about a water leak in the bathroom. John, with phone to his ear, walked into the bathroom and closed the door. Bathrooms and toilets seem to have taken up a significant role in his life.

Five minutes later the maestro was opening a deck of Bicycle cards. I asked him what card game he was playing with the Cleveland accountant back in Georgetown at Blues Alley.

"Why, are you a card player, a gambler?" he countered.

"Yuh. I like to play cards and gamble, but I couldn't figure out what the hell you were playing. Looked to me like high-low-jack."

"Tonk; some call it tunk. It's a little like high-low-jack, and it's a money game."

"Ah, I like that name, tonk; sounds like a social disease."

"It could become a disease or addiction, I guess."

He slyly gave me the eye. "As you can see, I just happen to have a deck of cards. I can show you how to play tonk in five minutes."

"Really..."

"Really." He paused. "You got some of them Rhode Island greenbacks in your pocket?"

At 0200 hours the Whale was sound asleep. The TV was on with the sound off. While dealing a hand of tonk, I asked John if he liked reggae music?

"I like Bob Marley."

"The best, but he's dead."

"Yes he is. Shiiit, most all of the music I listen to, the artists are dead. Bob Marley's wife and other family members carry on the cause."

"So, you know he was a conscious person. A true Rasta, Rastafarian."

"I do." John replied, "I feel that vibe. It is gen u ine. Jah Rastafari, mon."

"You sound Jamaican, John."

"You better believe I do." He had some kind of cane that made noise and he pounded it on the floor.

"Ya know, I go to Jamaica a lot. I could talk with the folks that run Reggae Sunsplash."

"Yeh, Reggae Sunsplash. That's a big annual shindig down there, ain't it?"

"Yes. Big, very big. The whole island shows up. Crowds around a hundred thousand. Maybe I could arrange something for you."

"Wouldn't that be sumpthin." He thought for a second. "I'd like to play with Bob Marley's wife – his widow – Rita Marley. And the kids. Think you could hook us up?"

"Want me to try?"

"Yeah, go for it. Sky is the limit. See if you can get a date. Don't worry about details. That's Whale's job."

After playing tonk for a while, I said, "I love listening to 'Manteca.' Everything about it fits perfect."

John nodded. "It took me, Chano Pozo, and another cat, cannot remember his name..."

"Walter Gil Fuller."

"Yeh, that's right, Gil Fuller," John confirmed. "Very good, David. I wrote the bridge. It took us about fifteen minutes to compose that piece. On a napkin."

"How professional that you thought to use a napkin." I looked across the table. He was drawing from my homemade spliff and had this shit-eating grin on his face, his palms open. "What does 'Manteca' mean?" I asked.

"Lard, in Spanish."

"Lard, like fat?"

"Yeh, like fat."

"And that's it? It's gotta have another meaning?"

"It does. Manteca's a hip name for marchin powder – cocaine."

"So, what's the idea of the song?"

"Well, you listen to it, David."

"I will. I have. But I'd like to hear your take."

John smiled. "It's the voice of cocaine – takes you through all the emotions, musically, you know, and makes the listener understand that that white yayo is the devil's brew – worse than a bad thing, got six-six-six written all over it."

"OK, Mr. Gillespie, I get it. Thank you for the detailed explanation."

"Well, understand this: I don't know hardly nuthin about that shit; all hearsay and seesay, see."

"Really?"

"Dead serious."

Photo by Ken Franckling © 1988.
Miles Davis and Kenny Garrett – calling and responding.

Narragansett Inn, RI

The Whale invited me to attend a private gig at the Narragansett Inn in Narragansett, RI, along Narragansett Bay. "The owner is a trumpet player and a huge Dizzy fan. So, we've agreed to bring the quintet and make everybody happy. Why don't you come down?"

Prior to driving to Narragansett, I had some minor surgery on my shoulder. Lots of stitches and soreness, but that wasn't gonna deter me from going.

The hotel was located across the street from a mile-long wall that connects to a Rhode Island institution called The Towers. On a feisty high tide, the waves come bouncing off that wall like gangbusters. Powerful, scenic sight.

I drove down with Paul Staiti and his wife, Barbara, and my friend Rachel. Upon arriving, while walking toward the entrance, we could see through a large bay window. There's Dizzy standing tall, framed through that glass in the center of an impromptu stage, horn held high. Could barely make out the top shelf of quality liquor bottles in the bar, set on the far wall. What an image of Dizzy Gillespie, in all his glory, in this quaint setting. Wish I had a camera.

The evening was an informal acoustical affair, lots of boozin and joking around. Dizzy had to be suffering from some kind of sinus condition because, on several occasions, he'd point his horn to the floor and shake saliva out. I've seen him doing that more than once. Not exactly a romantic move. Sam Rivers had the longest solo I've ever heard him play. It was a neo-Coltrane sound, stretched out, far out, awkward and hard to the ear, hard to understand, for me anyway. Then, in a surprise moment, from out of nowhere, the motel owner appeared on the makeshift stage, and joined the band as they played "Night in Tunisia." Could have been the greatest moment in his life.

During the break I headed to the men's room (uh oh). As I was walked in, I almost collided with the owner, who was walking out. I told him he did a great job playing his trumpet. He was all smiles and then slapped me on the shoulder, hard, right on the spot where I had the surgery. Will never forget that god-awful pain. Never ever. The guy was about as sick as I was.

Little did I know that just prior to my arrival at the lavatory, Paul Staiti had been in there. Paul told me that, when he walked in, Dizzy was standing at the commode taking a leak. "All of a sudden he let's out this enormous fart."

"What?"

"Man, it was loud, I'm tellin ya. I looked at Dizzy and asked him, 'B-Flat?'"

Narragansett was the last time I saw Sam Rivers. Something happened between John and him that broke the chord.

Just before leaving, I told John that I spoke to the producer of Reggae Sunspash.

Newport Jazz Festival

John was on the phone sermonizing from Englewood. "Listen up homeboy, I'm gonna tell ya some info bout your wonderful little Ocean State of Rhode Island and the town of Newport."

"What's that, boss?"

"Back in early American history before the Civil War, Newport was a port of call for slave tradin, part of the African/Caribbean triangle, and that's no mutha f--kin lie, Cracker. Tradin rum and sellin black, Nigga flesh. This is what I'm talkin about. And you live there."

"I know about that. Hate me."

"Dat's right." He paused long enough to wheeze. "And I'm gonna be playin there. You gonna come to Newport to see me at the Newport Jazz Festival?"

When it's a clear August Rhode Island beach day, you've got the world on a string. That's exactly how I felt when I met John and Charley at the Viking Hotel overlooking downtown Newport with it's quaint shops and bistros. Newport is cool, both a navy town and home for the New York blingers, those elites that built their opulence around Thames Street. The first few Jazz Festivals were held in town, next to the Tennis Hall of Fame, at a well-groomed baseball field called Freebody Park. After a few disturbances, the event moved around, until it found its permanent residence at Fort Adams State Park.

We drove to the venue in a big, black Cadillac limo (chariot). The chauffeur really knew the back roads, cuz we ran into no traffic from downtown Newport all the way to the Festival grounds at Fort Adams, while the rest of the city was grid-locked.

Along the entrance to the Park is Hammersmith Farm, where Jackie Bouvier Kennedy lived. The estate is framed at the top of a hill with thoroughbreds lazing under tall, shady green trees. A little further up the road is Newport Country Club, a perfect piece of golfing ground laid out in the fashion of arid links that sprawl along Britain's shoreline. Newport CC was a favorite of President Eisenhower.

Ten thousand jazz fans were crammed into Fort Adams. I was keeping an eye on Charley; it was as though he knew everyone in attendance. Besides being a social director and great at giving road directions, the Whale was a savvy agent for Dizzy. He was abuzz – shaking hands, hugging, laughing and reminiscing – an opportunity to network with music people from all over the world, a chance to set up future engagements.

The day's billing was an all-star lineup of Branford and Wynton Marsalis, Mel Tormé, Dave Brubeck, and George Shearing, with Dizzy and the quintet closing the gig. There were musicians, photographers and reporters milling about. My pass was on a lanyard and had my name on it and gave me entrée anywhere.

I spotted Mr. George Wein sitting on the other side of the stage. He is a veteran of the nightclub scene and founder of the Newport Jazz Festival, first held in 1954. The event, normally held during the second weekend of August, has become a musical institution. Wein also founded the Newport Folk Festival in 1959, which runs two weeks prior to the Jazz Festival.

I was mesmerized by the smooth voice of Mel Tormé, a genius at phrasing. Having the chance to stand so close, I could just about reach out and touch him. I swear, it felt as though he was singing to me. Like Dizzy, "The Velvet Fog" was a consummate performer, romancing the audience with funny stories. Yet his personna was 180 degrees different from Dizzy. Dizzy was a diva. Mel Tormé seemed harmless, his talking voice almost squeeky, his form nonathletic somewhere between buff and chubby. Guess what; the crowd loved him.

From my vantage point on the stage, I could see countless rows of people decked out on blankets, some dressed only in bathing suits. A throng. This mass of humanity ran all the way back to the salt water of Narragansett Bay. The foreground, which is a cove, was packed with boats and yachts, all in party mode. Along the sides and in the back were a variety of tented concession stands selling food and t-shirts, records and paraphernalia. The joint was jumpin. Ya could feel and smell it. Jazz lives.

John had his own portable trailer set behind the

red-bricked Fort Adams stage. George Wein brought in several artsy posters for John to sign.

After Mr. Wein left, a magazine reporter entered the trailer. I could tell by the gist of his questions and statements that John was uncomfortable. The reporter said, "Rumor has it that you don't take kindly to Louis Armstrong – that you think he's an Uncle Tom..."

"Whoa, whoa, stop right there. That comment is a big ole bad lie. And for the record, it's bullshit and preposterous. Louis Armstrong, besides being a brilliant performer, has done more for the black man,..." John coughed. "...the Negra, than most any freedom fighter." He gave the reporter a contrary look and said, "Hey, I gotta get ready for work, so you'll have to excuse me. Thanks for stopping by."

Things got real quiet. I asked John, "Where do you suppose that guy came from?"

He scanned the room and frowned. "Don't know. Shit, I ain't been hit on like that in a while, man. I'll give em the benefit of the doubt. Ya know, many years ago 'Pops' was playin with me and he had trouble handlin the bebop variations and nuances. I'm tryin to explain that to you in layman's terms, and he may have said something critical of bop. But that ain't got nothin at all to do with love and respect."

A new saxophonist was with the quintet: Ron Halloway. His smile was as broad as Ignascio Barroa's.

I met Mona Freeman that glorious afternoon. John introduced her as his mentor into the Bahá'í faith.

A lovely, pleasant lady who chain smoked. Shortly after John's set, he spent quite a bit of time with a contingency of Bahá'ians; then Mona and he headed off to Cape Cod. They truly seemed spiritually linked as they disappeared into the shadows of a tunnel in the great fort.

The Festival was over. Workmen were breaking down the stage.

Author and son Adam at the '89 Newport Jazz Festival. That's 28 years ago!

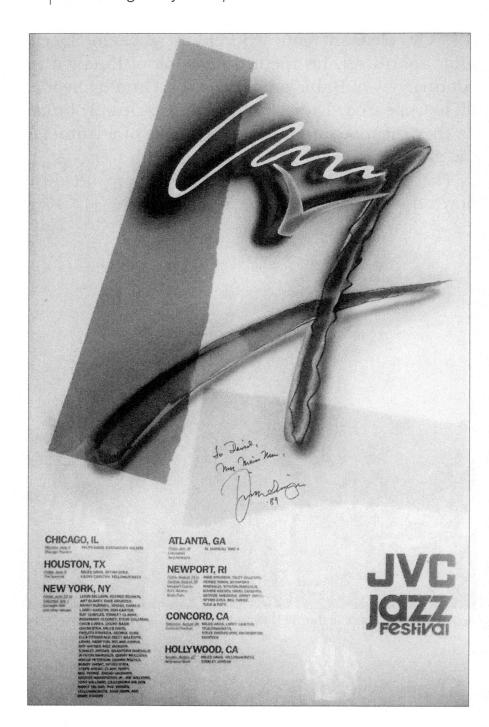

Flynn Theater, Burlington, VT

My Woonsocket friend Paul Staiti, another tennis pro, had a student who owned a beautiful summer home in Woodstock, VT, and the student agreed to let us take over the house for a few days. John was playing at the Flynn Theater in nearby Burlington. Charley and Ginny stayed with us. The Flynn Theater folks put John up at a fancy hotel in town.

After the gig, a chauffeur, dressed in a tuxedo, drove us in an antique Bentley from the theater to a private party at the downtown Burlington hotel where John was staying. John found a balloon in the back seat and, halfway to our destination, asked the driver to let us off. Once on the sidewalk, he declared, "I wanna smoke some of that Jamaican good stuff. Privately." He lit that baby spliff up in a hurry, took a deep draw, and while exhaling, said, "Uh huh, that's what the doctor ordered." He looked around. "Wonder what might happen if a Burlington cop car drives by and spots us?"

Now, this party was in honor of the jovial maestro, and the gentry was anxiously awaiting his arrival. Back on the street, the ganj had set in and we were feeling no pain. We were like the Three Stooges – or three school kids – all gerped on the good life, being simple, stupid, and as free as the air-filled balloon.

As we walked, John told us about a day, not long ago, when he returned to his hometown. He spotted a sign that read "Cheraw, SC, Home of Dizzy Gillespie." Shortly thereafter, Dizzy drove over to a barber shop and the owner said he wouldn't cut his hair. One of the patrons recognized him and the barber changed his mind. John stopped and looked at us. "Well, so did I."

Try to picture this: John is strolling down this avenue and adroitly bouncing that balloon from his head to his feet with a temporary stop on his stomach. He keeps working that balloon all the way to the hotel. When the elevator door opens, the balloon flies off. It's about to hit the floor when Dizzy quickly doubles over, saves it, and balances it again from his head. What? I thought he was a musician, not a contortionist.

Meanwhile, Paul forgot to put film in his camera.

I don't remember much about that party, or the performance for that matter. I recall enjoying Ron Holloway's solos on sax. Ron, who replaced Sam Rivers, does not read music, yet fit in tightly with the quintet. Oh yes, they had delicious hors d'oeurves with an open bar. I can picture some of the dignitaries, all worried, pouncing on the late-arriving maestro, concerned where he disappeared to.

And I remember the beautiful home we stayed in. While lying in bed late that night with a cool, fresh Vermont breeze blowing through my open window, I popped in my earplugs and listened to an album featuring the British pianist Marian McPartland and Dizzy (The Jazz Alliance TJA-12042-2/1993). The mix of Marian's British accent with Dizzy's southern drawl is priceless; it's lovable, funny and instructive. Dizzy not only blows his trumpet, he also plays piano with Marian. Not for nuthin and in all due respect to Marian, I thought Dizzy was a better piano player. He's that versatile. By playing and understanding the piano, it made him a more perfect composer. Anyone – musician or layman – who listens to this album will become better versed in music. There are several memorable sound bites:

Dizzy suggests that the media coined the term, *bebop.*

They laugh about a song title, "Max is Making Wax."

Marion plays Charley Lake's favorite Dizzy creation, "Con Alma."

Dizzy waxes about his Bahá'í faith. "Everyone is welcome; there's only one creator."

They play Ellington's "In a Mellow Tone." Dizzy said, "When performing with Duke, use what you know, and follow him."

In the book *Steppenwolf,* written by Hermann Hesse, the author defines "immortals" as those that have passed to the "otherside." Hesse's main *immortal* reference is the classical composer Wolfgang Amadeus Mozart, a most prolific master of music; and because of his greatness, Mozart is referred to as one of the *immortals.* I'm thinking both the Duke and John sit in the same box seats as Amadeus."

Photo by Ken Franckling © 1987
Boss blowin light bubbles.

The Goat Island Sheridan, Newport, RI

As a member of the Independent Insurance Agents of Rhode Island, I was invited to serve on their entertainment committee. They were excited to know I could hire Dizzy to play at the their annual convention. For a tidy sum, Dizzy agreed to bring in the quintet and do an hour-and-a-half performance.

I picked up John that morning at T. F. Greene airport in Warwick. He walked into the luggage area wearing a black beret and holding what he called his "shaker stick," a wooden walking cane completely covered with Coke bottle caps nailed into the shaft. (John told me he manages to lose, misplace, or give them away, and has a pal who keeps banging out replacements.) Every time John shook the stick, he made music with it. He walked around Newport for two days shaking that schtick stick noisemaker, and even used it in his performance. By the time he left, everyone in Newport knew he was there. Even the gray ghosts of slave traders past.

I had the distinction of introducing the Dizzy Gillespie Quintet, and presented John with a handsome purple African hat with intricate designs. He absolutely loved it and, in return, handed me the black beret he was wearing. He said, "This here chapeau, mon ami, is a symbol of bebop jazz." I still cherish that beret. When I look inside, I see, entwined in the thread, strands of his gray hair.

After the quintet's first number, the audience lost interest in the music. What? In retrospect, John's music was not meant for a group of business suits intent on networking. Still, they should have known this was not the place to be mouthing off while a legendary musical virtuoso was performing. Turned out to be the most discourteous audience I've ever seen John play in front of.

I was so embarrassed and I think John was annoyed. He laughed and showed me the check he was paid. "Hey, you got us a good night's pay."

Later that night we drove into downcity Providence. On the way, Charley said, "Tell David about your experience with the Bahá'í priests in Haifa."

"Oooh, that was somethin else." John's voice was filled with enthusiasm. "I get this invitation – a formal letter from the Bahá'í headquarters in Haifa. That's Israel, ya know. They want me to fly over for a session at their temple. I, I, I wasn't too sure about that one." He looked at Charley. "But, the Whale encouraged me and we both went.

"So now we're in Haifa. Actually, we're up on Mount Carmel. Haifa is at the base of the mountain. You shoulda seen this place. It looks like pictures of ancient Rome. We're sittin in this waiting room of this fancy temple, the Bahá'í's Universal House of Justice. A gentleman comes in and says, 'Mr. Gillespie, please follow me.' I'm summoned. Shit man, I was nervous as hell."

Charley piped in. "He was nervous, all right. Never seen him like this."

"Yeh, you said I looked white."

"You did."

"So we walks into this beautiful room and there are nine distinguished-looking gentlemen sitting in a circle – faces that came from different places in the world. Can you picture that, David?" He shakes the stick. "Now these gentlemen ask me to sit in the middle of the room. Which I did, right? Then the main man stands up and mellifluously tells me they understand I'm a world traveler and they would like to get my thoughts and observations – what I'm seein and thinkin. That's it. That's all."

"What did you tell them?"

"You can guess what I told them. I gave them the straight skinny as to what's happening in politics, poverty and racial issues – that we gotta do a better job taking care of each other, and the environment. Shit, we had a good time. They was real people."

I asked John, "How does a Southerner from South Carolina ever become a member of the Bahá'í faith?"

"To me, it's the most beautiful and logical faith, because it welcomes everybody and anybody, regardless of who you may believe is a prophet, a leader, or even a son of God."

I brought Charley and John to a Providence landmark, the Haven Brothers Diner, an all-night chow wagon adjacent to Providence City Hall. We feasted on weiners, the popular Rhode Island skinny hot dogs topped with mustard, onions, a meat sauce, and a sprinkle of celery salt. The late-night crowd hungers for these dogs. John was right at home, shaking his schtick stick and chatting with a bunch of locals.

On the drive back to Newport, while we're cruisin over the Jamestown Bridge, John tapped me on the shoulder. "I told them folk in Haifa one other thing..."

"The Bahá'ís?"

He leaned in, head closer to me, eyes a tad blood-shot. "Yeh, that's right. Them good fellas back in Haifa."

"Well, what else did you tell them, John?"

A somber sly smile crossed that endless face. "Jazz is too good for Americans."

Our moods abruptly changed; smiles turned to frowns. It's the most controversial comment I ever heard from him. I was tempted to challenge, but I didn't. I had too much respect for his feelings and experiences. His statement was not hateful, but one of disappointment and sadness. I thought of the phrase "Never mock an Indian until you've walked a mile in his moccasins." John walked with Martin Luther King, got whacked in the head with a coke bottle, understood politricks. And he was always teaching...

I keep repeating these words to myself: "Everythin's cool if Malcolm says so…" Dizzy says this on the *Dizzy For President* album (Douglas Music ADC1), while he's joking around with James Moody before they play "Black Orpheus." "Everythin's cool if Malcolm says so…"

Photo by R. Ferrier.
Author presenting gift at Goat Island Sheridan. Looks like Dizzy is about to ask, "Is it true you broke my horn?"

Blue Note Jazz Club
Greenwich Village, NY, NY
(first night)

It was late at night, the phone rang. It was John. He was singing, "I love Paris in the springtime... Next week I'm hopping on a Concorde jet to Paree, see. Oh yeh, an away game. I score twenty-five large and back home in two days.

"Then I'm doing the Blue Note in the Village for two nights. If you want to come, c'mon in. The Whale won't be here for those engagements. You can stay at my place."

What an offer. I'm nuts about New York City. And that comes from a die-hard Red Sox fan. Called John back the following night and told him, "I'm going to drive in and stay at my Uncle Harry's apartment in the City. Would it be all right to bring him to the second night gig?"

"You'll be on the guest list. Just tell them when you walk in the door. I'll have you set up for the second set, so your uncle can hang out with us. Then, later you can drive me home."

"Sounds good, John. Thanks."

I walked in the front door of the world-renowned Blue Note Jazz Club and there was John sitting all by his lonesome at a table to my right, against a bulkhead and near a window where he could look out and see the action on the street. The maestro loved to eat, and talk about food. He was fingering a basket of warm buns and butter. There was a plateful of shrimp gumbo with rice, a salad and a bottle of San Pellegrino. He stood up, lookin dapper in an open Hawaiian shirt and a tweed sports jacket. He shook my hand, gave me a hug, and I handed him a book about Bob Marley.

"Thanks for the book. Man, you got me thinkin about that prophet. I'll read it quick. Ya know, it could be bad, real bad, playin with them Marleys. That Sunsplash Festival down there in JA, right next to Cuba..., why I could bring somma my Cuba boys over by boat and we could hook up."

Looking at the glass of San Pellegrino John drank from, I couldn't help but ask, "I notice you don't drink booze."

"Yeah, that's right."

"How come?

"I did, but over time I found too many downsides. Messes with your insides, like your liver. Seen so many cats lose to booze. Not crazy about the buzz, like it can't even compare to weed. And you just don't see Bahá'í folks drinkin. That pretty much sums it up. Come to think about it, I don't recall you drinking alcohol."

"Oh, I do. But not much. I prefer a drink now and then. Like a beer with pizza or seafood. But, I hate the effects of getting drunk and I hate to puke."

"That's right. Me too. I like eatin so much, I wanna keep that food in me."

"To tell ya the truth, John, I hate to adulterate my high when smokin good ganj."

"That's right. See, we gots stuff in common, don't we?" He nodded. "Hey, uh, I wanted to tell ya they took a picture of me wearin your purple African hat, and it's gonna be on the cover of American Airlines magazine."

"I hope you're under it."

The Blue Note Jazz Club is unique because of it's rectangular shape with the stage running almost the length of the room. The old, torn down Celebrity Jazz Club in Providence was like that.

It was special being with Dizzy at the Blue Note, this institution of music. The club's ambiance is also special, a singular New York intimacy that permeates from the Big Apple dialect of the coat check chick to the walls which showcase photos of legends that have performed on this stage. It was a room filled with angels, drum brush sounds, jazz fragranced with romantic whispers, Dizzy holding horn adorned with a golden halo.

After the first set, we were standing in front of the coat check room and John was talking about a dental appointment he had in the City that afternoon. The dentist was checking on his chops. Seems he was having an embouchure problem because his chops were slightly out of alignment with the mouthpiece of his horn.

John was all caught up in the explanation when we were interrupted by this short, shapely, blonde-haired dame who looked to be in her forties. She just walked in the front door, approached John, pointed her finger at him, and, with a thick British accent, she said, "I know you. I've got a limousine parked out front." She grabbed John's hand and tried to pull him toward the door. "I'm going to walk you out to my limo and take you around the world."

"No, no, no," John said. "We cain't be doin dat."

"What do you mean?"

"I go back on in a half hour."

"That's all right. We have time."

"Look lady, this ain't gonna work."

She repeated, "Oh, yes it will. We've got time."

"You don't understand; I'm a married man."

The situation had turned from comical to awkward.

"That's no big deal; I'm a married woman."

"Look lady. Let me tell you somethin..."

"What's that?"

"Truth be known, I really don't like white people!"

"What?" She looked at John all vexed, then at me, and pointed. "He's white."

And John replied, "No he ain't."

Midway through the second set, Dizzy said, "Tonight, we have a special guest in the audience. Ladies and gentlemen, at this time, I'd like to introduce former heavyweight champion of the world, all the way from Philadelphia, Mr. 'Smokin' Joe Frazier."

A spotlight panned across the room. To our left, to our right, directly at us, behind us. Finally it re-illuminated Dizz. He opened the palm of his hands. "Damn, I forgot. That was last night."

The set ran without a hitch, perfectly tight. No after-gig partying. John Lee drove the maestro home.

Blue Note (2nd night)

The brother of my mother, ninety-two year old Uncle Harry, and I left his apartment at 30 Park Ave and pulled into the indoor parking garage across the street from the Blue Note. Harry, who my mother called "a pollack in a fishbowl," was as much a character as John Birks. He had spent his life selling clothes to the clergy and undertakers.

No sooner were we at our table, even before sitting down, he instructed our waitress to bring him a bowl of French onion soup. As she walked away, Harry yelled, "Hot."

Uncle was all fired up, telling people he's friends with Mr. *Gillepsy*, and they can expect a good show. He was handing out business cards. Within minutes, there are bread crumbs, soup stains, and a glob of butter on the tablecloth.

The Quintet came on stage and Uncle fell into a trance. After the opening number, Dizzy joined the boys. He pulled the Joe Frazier prank on the late crowd, which confused the shit out of Harry. He kept poking me. "Where's Joe Frazier, where is he?"

After the show, it was about 2am, and Uncle Harry was still totally stoked. I walked him upstairs for a head call (I swear he farted while taking his leak), then led him to John's dressing room.

There was the sweet aroma of herbal essence in the room. Uncle Harry gave me an elbow to the ribs and then a wink. I intro'd Harry to John. They embraced like long lost cousins and Harry was calling him Mr. Gillepsy. Before John can respond, Harry pulled a yellow cloth measuring tape out of his pocket and strapped it across John's broad shoulders. "You're a 44 ... athletic; I've got some sport coats that are perfect for ya. Ya can take that to the bank, by Jesus." He then handed John a stack of his business cards.

Shortly thereafter, Harry asked John if he wanted to go out for a bite. I was concerned that having the two of them in the same dining room could create a major disaster.[1] Then, in a matter of moments, Harry got tired. We walked him out to the front of the club and put him in a taxi. Wasn't sure if John wanted to adopt Uncle or dial 911.

John and I drove through the city taking in all the late night action. We crossed the George Washington Bridge bound for Englewood, NJ, which is just north of Fort Lee, and then drove along the cliffs overlooking the Hudson. As we neared John's street, East Palisades Road, he pointed at a house, a fancy place. "That's where Sarah Vaughn lives." We pulled into his

---

[1] I spoke with John Dimitriou, owner of Dimitriou's Jazz Alley in Seattle. I was trying to determine if Dizzy's last performance was at his club, when the conversation somehow switched to food. He said he booked Dizzy for a New Year's Eve gig several years ago. "It was a buffet affair and Dizzy made sure he was first in line. At one point Dizzy is holding a ladle filled with jello, and completely missed the plate in his attempt to place the contents on his stacked dish. The jello hit the floor. Dizzy looked around and saw that I spotted the mishap and, with one nonchalant kick, he deftly swept the entire mess under the table – not an easy feat with jello. He nodded and sat down at his table."

driveway, which was aside his modest ranch house. There were two huge dumpsters in the driveway. He opened one. It was packed with gifts - camera's, photo albums, books, bottles, clothing, and sun glasses. Wouldn't have been surprised to see a blonde-haired British dame sitting in there. In the other dumpster were thousands of letters. He deposited some of that night's booty.

Lorraine appeared at the side door dressed in pajamas and a bathrobe. It was late. She was courteous, but abrupt. I bid my goodbyes and headed back to Rhode Island. On the drive, I was conjuring up the sight of Uncle Harry and John together. Then I remembered once hearing a recording that was called "The Farting Contest." It takes place in Toronto's Maple Leaf Garden and the narrator has a heavy British accent. I picture Uncle Harry and John as contestants.

Uncle Harry chowin down.

Photo by author.

A Night in Woonsocket at Chan's
by John Chan

It was a Monday afternoon, February 15, 1988. As the nation celebrated Washington's birthday, we at Chan's were preparing for a very special guest, the Father of Bebop jazz, Dizzy Gillespie.

John Birks "Dizzy" Gillespie, legendary jazz trumpeter extraordinaire, walked into Chan's Fine Oriental Dining in beautiful downtown Woonsocket, Rhode Island, accompanied by his longtime road manager, Charles Lake, affectionately known as "The Whale."

Dizzy brought along his world-class all-star band featuring Cuban-born Ignaciao Barroa to keep time on the drums, walking the bassline was John Lee, the fabulous Ed Cherry on guitar, and Sam Rivers on reeds. Then came Dizzy with his broad smile, signature bent horn, and giant balloon cheeks. What a sight. Maestro was wearing red plaid pants and a pink sports jacket. He tapped the microphone and Chan's lit up.

After the sound check came our feast of Chinese delicacies featuring roast duck and fresh ginger lobster (Dizzy's favorite). Dining in Chan's private beaded room provided the perfect ambiance to hear some of Dizzy's wonderful stories. At seventy years young he was still on the top of his game.

During the Chan's dining experience, we were briefly interrupted by a visit from Woonsocket's Mardi

Gras royal couple, King Jayce and Queen Michelle. It was a fun encounter as the King knelt in front of the King of Jazz. In return Dizzy kissed the King's ring and graciously bowed to the Queen.

Dizzy's performance was brilliant and captivating. He was witty and extremely engaging with the audience. At the end of the gig, jazz fan Charlie Sokoloff and I told Dizzy that we weren't going to let him off the stage unless he played "A Night in Tunisia." Dizzy smiled and played "Tunisia" to a standing ovation.

My favorite Dizzy experience happened the following year when Dizzy returned to Rhode Island to perform for the alumni at Bryant University in nearby Smithfield. On his way back to the airport, Dizzy instructed his chauffeur to detour to Woonsocket. That Sunday afternoon, in walked my friend the great Dizzy Gillespie unannounced. I said, "This is a pleasant surprise. What are you doing here Dizz?"

"Hey man, I was in your neighborhood and remembered the good times we had. AND, I'm craving some more of your delicious chicken wings and teriyaki."

So, I fixed a big box of take-out Chinese for the entire band to feast on for the ride to the airport.

Happy 100th birthday Dizzy."

Photo courtesy of the Charles Lake Collection.
Dizzy and John Chan between sets.

Courtesy of the Charles Lake Collection.
Dizzy burning at Chan's wearing author's
African hat.

Oil painting by John Chan © 2017

See it in full color at www.BraveDownBooks.com.

Regatta Bar
Harvard Square, Cambridge, MA

While driving into Boston I listened to Ron Della Chiesa's radio program, *Music America,* on WGBH in Cambridge. Ron spent a good portion of his three hour slot interviewing Dizzy.

Arriving at the Regatta Bar, I found part of the entourage, and everyone was looking for Dizzy. The Whale said, "Have no fear; whenever Birks is in Boston, he'll disappear for a few hours and head over to Legal Sea Food. Guarantee you he's chompin away on fried clams and lobster."

After the two-set gig and back in a large suite provided by the Regatta, I said, "John, I'm puzzled. I know Charlie Parker and you were like bacon and eggs and, for some reason, we've never talked about him. How come?"

"I don't know. That is strange because I think about Bird all the time."

"What do you think about?"

"Wishin I was as smart as him."

"C'mon John, you cannot be serious?"

"I'm dead serious. He was a brilliant man. Besides his alto virtuosity, you shoulda heard him talk. What a vocabulary. When Bird was around, I became a listener. Shit, man, he coulda outspoke Paul Robison. It kills me at times thinkin about what coulda been.

Lotta times I just get sad thinkin about Charlie Chan Parker."

"Charlie Chan?"

"Yeh, man. For some productions, he went under the name of Charlie Chan cuz he wasn't licensed, ya see – like uncertified to perform in New York City. So he did shit, like recordings, under that false name – Mr. Chan. Chan was Bird's wife's first name."

As far as drugs are concerned, John said, "Believe me, everyone knew he was goin way overboard takin shit, and I did my best tryin to talk to him. But I ain't my brother's keeper. And, I wasn't exactly close to the cloth neither, smokin weed, ya know." John shook his head. "Bird actually rationalized his bad habits by sayin – get this – he's setting an example for folks as to what they should not let happen to them. Crazy, huh? For many, the urge overpowers the intellect." John's arms spread and he opened both palms in resignation. "Let's play some tonk."

After a few hands, John said, "I've fallen into a mellow mood."

I looked across the messy table covered with cookies, crumbs, cheese and crackers, glasses and eye glasses, along with an ash tray holding a stubby roach. John was sprawled across his chair, a spliff dangling from his lips, so relaxed I could see an extra droop in his cheeks. He was carefully arranging his cards, whispering to himself and making facial expressions. He placed the cards on the table, his face long and sad. "I miss Lalo."[2]

"Lalo?"

He looked surprised. "You're suppose to know who Lalo is." John sounded like a scolding junior high school teacher.

"Hey boss, there's a lot I don't know, ya know."

"Well, Lalo Schifrin is an amazing man. I bet by the next time I see you, you'll know plenty about him."

We quit at about five that morning and sacked out till eight. The Whale woke us up. He had to hustle John to Logan Airport for a flight back to the city. As we were leaving, Charley said, "Hey, check this out." He rolled over a cushion on one of the sofas and found $25,000 in cold, hard cash held together by a rubber band.

"Hey Birks, you want this, or what?"

As Dizzy walked out of the room, I could hear him choking on laughter.

Charley looked at me with this face. "Ya know what I am? I'm a f--kin housekeeper, that's what I am, and Armenian horn-sitter. If I don't clean house every- where we go, we'd go broke from the bread he's left behind."

---

[2] Boris Claudio "Lalo" Schifrin is an Argentinian who now lives in California. A child prodigy at the piano, he's gained fame as a composer and arranger. To acknowledge all of his accomplishments would be an injustice in such short space. To list a few, Lalo has won four Grammy Awards and six Oscar nominations. A few of his film scores – *Cool Hand Luke, Bullitt,* and *Love Story;* TV scores include *Mission Impossible, Planet of the Apes, Starsky and Hutch.* He has composed, arranged and played in ten albums with Dizzy, most noted are *Gillespiana, The New Continent,* and *Dizzy on the French Riviera.* They also played and traveled together as part of a quartet, as well as Dizzy's United Nations Orchestra.

Dizzy and Spider Martin playing at Ciro's.

Ciro's, Boca Raton, FL

The Whale had a winter pad in Hollywood Beach, FL. I co-owned a condo in Boynton Beach. The two locations were about a half hour apart. John had no problem getting tropical in the winter, and Charley tried to set winter gigs in warm climates. As luck would have it, one Sunday when I was in Boynton Beach, Dizzy played at a restaurant called Ciro's in Boca Raton with saxophonist Spider Martin, an old friend, along with his son on drums, and a few sidemen.

As soon as I walked into Ciro's, there was Charley standing up at his table and waving me over. John was sitting with Tony Bennett and his brother. Just like that, south of the Mason-Dixon Line, I was breaking bread with two musical giants. The best part: everything was so easy-going, it was like cavorting with family.

Spider Martin pulled up a chair and sat between Tony and Dizzy. He discussed the set and asked Tony if he'd sing a few songs. Tony liked the idea … I think.

Spider said, "Hey Dizz, I've got a bunch of friends who've stopped by for tonight's gig, and they want to know the straight skinny about the Cab Calloway stabbing."

"Shiit, Spider, that was back in 1941. You expectin me to remember dat."

"C'mon, Dizz, what happened? You hit him with a spitball, right?"

"Hell no. That ain't it at all. Jonah Jones hit him with the spitball. This was during a radio broadcast. Cab, he was sooo pissed off, and fixin to blame the entire matter on me. Then we gets out in the lobby and he throws a slap at me. A love affair; that's all I'm sayin. We should put that crazy-ass story to rest."

The conversation took a quick turn, and now I was listening to John and Tony. It was like eavesdropping on Beethoven and Pavarotti. They were talking business. Dizzy was all wound up about having spaghetti at Chuck Mangione's mother's house in Rochester, and later recording a CD with the Rochester Philharmonic Orchestra led by John Dankworth. Dizzy mentioned that he'd be bringing the quintet along. I'm not too sure which was more important to him, the spaghetti or the music.

Not many people know that Tony Bennett is an accomplished painter. He was talking about the peace he feels while painting, and spontaneously asked, "Hey Dizz, how would you like me doing the album cover for the Dankworth event?"

"Tony, would you wanna do dat?"

"Absolutely."

"Good, good." They shook hands.

The album is entitled, *Dizzy Gillespie, The Symphony Sessions* (August 25, 1989, CDJ 698).

The cover illustration is painted by artiste Tony Bennett. All Gillespie compositions. In the notes is a photo of Tony Bennett with annotator Ron Della Chiesa. This photo was taken by the owner of the El Morocco restaurant in Worcester, MA. His name is Bobby Bayrouty, a huge jazz patron. I've attended several wonderful jazz nights at the El Morocco. One of my best friends, Larry Berk, introduced me to Ritchie Bayrouty, Bob's brother. Ritchie was always the most gracious host whenever we visited the restaurant.

The El Morocco hosted a surprise sixty-fifth birthday party for Charley Lake (after John had passed). The Artie Shaw Band, led by Brockton, MA, clarinetist Dick Johnson, performed at that gala event. Will never forget the startled look on Charley's face when he walked into the over-filled and silent room with Ginny and Ron Della Chiesa. God bless the Whale.

For we New Englanders, the El Morocco was a major jazz venue along with Lenny's on the Highway, the Celebrity Club and Bovi's in Rhode Island, and George Wein's Storyland in Cambridge. Then Chan's came along.

Sea Crest Hotel, Cape Cod, MA

Charley gave me his usual precise directions to the Sea Crest Beach Hotel in North Falmouth, where Dizzy united with one of his favorite jazz trumpet players, Lou Columbo. Dizzy called him a trumpet painter. Lou was from Rocky Marciano's hometown of Brockton and he was a funny guy, not only because of his stories, but by the way he told them with twisted facial expressions and animated gestures.

The Whale did a great job on this booking, rounding up some of New England's finest jazz artists. Gray Sargent on guitar, Ed Higgins on piano – or piana, as Dizz would say. Gary Johnson, the drummer; Marshall Wood on bass; and, of course, Lou and Dizzy rounding out the sextet. They were lined up across the stage.

It was a well-played set of music and the whitest gang I've ever seen John play with. I do not recall the musical selections, but I did notice Dizzy was not as animated as usual. Hell, he'd been on a rigorous schedule, traveling to over 300 gigs a year during the last decade, constantly in demand – on TV, in studios, doing interviews, and playing. I remember one night over a game of tonk, he told me he really didn't start making serious bread till he turned sixty-five. That sounded like he spent a long period of time graduating from his junior to senior year. I also noted he'd lost some weight. Must be following a healthier diet.

After the gig, I spent some time shooting the breeze with Gary Johnson and Gray Sargent. Took them a while to calm down, ecstatic from being on the stand with Dizzy.

Gary told me his dad, Dick Johnson, was out of town and bummed that he missed a chance to play with Dizzy. Dick, a virtuoso clarinetist and reed man, was selected by Artie Shaw to lead the Artie Shaw Orchestra. Artie thought Dick played the best clarinet ... ever. That night, Dick was off tending to other business.

Later, we caught up to Dizzy, who was standing by the door with Charley. "Ya know, I gotta tell ya, I'm bushed. Sleepin over at the Whale's tonight and heading out of Logan in the early morning. Got a doctor's appointment in the City."

Mechanics Hall, Worcester, MA

Quite the music venue, this Mechanics Hall. Built in 1857, it has fancy early American paintings set high on the walls, chandeliers, balconies, and a huge organ. Paul Staiti joined me, and this time he had film in his camera. Charley had us all sitting in the front row and, after the first number, I looked at Dizzy and pointed to my ears. He leaned into the mike and said, "The sound ain't right, is it?"

"No it ain't."

He countered, "Ya know, that's not a problem. This hall will be fine if we go acoustical." He looked at the sound man. "Shut it all down." And that's exactly what they did. The sound became pure as honey, and the Quintet performed for an hour and a half.

Later, I drove over to John's hotel, looking forward to a few hours of cards and communication.

Once we settled in, he said, "Well, whatya know, your ears got good grades tonight."

"Thank you, maestro."

"As soon as you gestured from your seat, I knew that sound was f--ked up."

"You sure fixed that problem quick."

"Show gots to go on, ya know. Ya know, the ear, I mean sound is so important, and there are so many variables."

"What do you mean?"

"Well tonight was a good example. That Hall was made for acoustical sound. We shoulda figured that out in advance. Now, compare it to the Newport Jazz Festival, an outside venue. If it wasn't for the sound technicians from JVC, so much would be sucked out, or in, by the atmosphere."

"I'm thinking about Erroll Garner's 'Concert by the Sea,'" I added.

"State of the art sound, right there. So, if you got a good ear, it can be as important as the artist himself. Lots to focus on, cuz each place is different; the sound check plays important. You can feel good you made a contribution tonight."

"I am feelin good, John."

John drew on his reefer and said, "Ya know, one thing..."

"What's that, John?"

"Too bad that gig with Bob Marley's family never panned out."

I shook my head. "No shit. Let me tell you what happened. Remember when I brought my Uncle Harry to see you at the Blue Note, and I told you I was going to Jamaica?"

"How could I forget your uncle? He's moved in to my bathroom."

"The next day I called Barrington, my Jamaican friend, for help. He arranged an appointment with Ronnie Burke, one of the founding fathers of Synergy, Inc., the company that produces Reggae Sunsplash."

"That's a good start."

"Yes, it was. What a trip. We drove from Montego Bay to Kingston in a beat-up Toyota rental car with no air-conditioning, east along the north coast to Saint Ann's Bay. That's where Marcus Garvey lived."

"I know all about Marcus."

"Barrington and I stopped in Nine Miles to see Bob Marley's childhood home and grave site. Then we shot up into the Blue Mountain Range. Unbelievable scenery, John; I'll never forget that drive. Thank god Barrington was with me because he's good at driving those mountain roads, all filled with pot holes the size of bunkers. He's no mapologist though, and we got lost on our way to Kingston."

"I can just see the two of you, stoned out of your minds on ganj. No wonder you got lost. Kinda wish I was there."

"No ganja for me that day, all business. Bottom line, I met with Ronnie Burke at his office in downtown Kingston. Turns out he loves jazz and was ecstatic about you playing Sunsplash. Swear to god. He tells me his next move is to contact Rita Marley and work things out with her. And, as soon as he knows something, he'll call me.

"I mean, I'm psyched. Imagine all of us flying over to JA. What an experience."

"So far, so good."

"I waited a month and got no call. That's about the time I brought you up to date. Remember, you said for me to keep trying and, if something breaks, you'd work it out with your schedule."

"Yup."

"So, I placed a call to Ronnie Burke and ended up speaking to some assistant who said she'd pass on the message. Another month goes by. I also called Barrington and he says to me, 'That's Jamaica time, mon.'

"Well, I waited and waited, and never got the call. I tried a few times but never connected with Burke again. Empty f--kin feeling, that's all I can say. Don't know what's the matter with those people. That could have been the best gig Sunsplash ever had. And it died going nowhere. Of all our wonderful experiences, that's the only one I regret..."

"Man, don't you go regrettin nothin. Shit like that happens all the time in this business.

"Just ask Charley. I suppose you coulda told me earlier. There's a few cats I mighta called. How come it took you so long to tell me?"

"I was embarrassed. I did not want to fail."

"Well, you never know. Maybe you'll get a call tomorrow."

"That sure would be nice." I changed course. "Ya know, John, I've been meaning to ask you for a while now..."

"What's that?"

"Well, I wonder at times, I mean, not for nothin, but what in God's name ever made you invite me to spend so much time with you. I mean, why me?"

He gave me a serious look, then expanded those cheeks, and said, "Now that's an interesting question. I could give you a silly-ass answer, but I won't, cuz we got more than a silly-ass friendship." He swigged on his tea. "I, I, I, I'm not one hundred percent sure why, cept there was an immediate connection. You made me laugh my ass off at Blues Alley. I liked talkin to you. I knew you loved the music; that was written all over your face. And, ya know, believe it or not, outside of music, I don't have much time to socialize, yet there's something special about spending time with people that are totally unrelated to music, but are on the same vibe. I can learn from you, and at the same time fill you up with music.

"Oh yeah, then, that night in Waterville Valley up there in the mountains, you told me you didn't play any instruments other than your ear. I always laughed at that one, picturing you with a horn coming outta your ear. Then you said your only art form is writing. So, I figured, along the way, I could teach you some music, and one day you'd write about me."

"Seriously?"

"No shit, seriously. When you're ready, when you've honed your skills, you'll do it. We've done pretty good so far, haven't we?" He smiled. "Destiny defined, David."

"C'mon man. I think you think you can hook up with a cracker like me and work me the way Jack

Benny worked Rochester."

He laughed and spit something in my direction, just like Uncle Harry. "Oo, oo, you got that right…"

"You're a bad mutha f--ka, John."

"And don't ya ever forget it, ya hear?"

"I sure do love ya, John."

"The feelin is mutual, David. I'm blessed with so many friends, real people, and you are one of them. There really is nothin better'n love."

"Thank you, John. You make me very happy."

I headed back to Woonsocket. It was eight in the morning. I was pumped up; felt like I was just getting up after a good night's sleep. I knew I had a true friend.

Not long after the Mechanics Hall engagement, I received a late-night call from John. He got right to the point. "I've been diagnosed with pancreatic cancer."

There were a few seconds of silence, enough time to process that pancreatic problems are not good. "How bad? What did they tell you, John?" I wanted to reach through the phone and hug him, never let him go.

"Not good."

"Oh my God, John, I don't know what to say. I care so much, and I'm worried."

"I know. Not much else to say. I wanted to call and let you know."

"Thanks, John. You know I love you."

"Love you too, David. Hey, I ain't a gonna yet, ya know. I still got plans. I'm gonna do a one-month program at the Blue Note with a special guest each night. Then we'll see. Maybe something magical might happen."

"Sure hope so. I'll be thinking of you and hoping things turn out for the best."

"Thank you."

And that was it. "Thank you!" He's thanking me. I sat helpless and numbed, listening to the buzz of the phone. I should have said more, something more consoling, profound, something poetic, something that would make the cancer go away. I don't know.

Photo courtesy of Paul Stati.
"Mirror Image" Taken in John's dressing room at Mechanics Hall prior to the Quintet's performance. His pensive countenance says it all. When Paul developed the frame, he said to me, "Check out the mug in the mirror." It was the last time I saw John.

Cathedral of St. John The Divine, NY

He did exactly what he said he'd do and performed at the Blue Note for one solid month, with a different guest artist each night – giants of the music world. It pains me to no end visualizing those nightly events of celebration and sadness. F--king requiems of sorts; the urge to do one more song, one more note. He did a few other gigs. The Whale said he only played his Jew's harp and that funny looking shaker stick.

Then the inevitable call came in from Charley. John passed on January 6, 1993. The Whale told me it was Lorraine's birthday. I knew him for seven years, ten months, and six days. John was born on October 21, 1917. Seventy-five fleeting, brilliantly filled, miraculous years.

Atlantic Ocean tides roll into Charley Lake's back yard on Broadsound Avenue in Revere Beach. The Whale has a cozy two-story cottage that overflows with memorabilia. It's like a Dizzy Gillespie jazz museum filled with vinyls, CDs, programs, photos and gifts from all over the world. Charley has collected several beautiful whale carvings. His convertible has a Massachusetts license plate that reads WHALE.

On Monday, 1/11/93, I drove to Revere Beach and stayed the night with Charley. It was a quiet, somber evening of reflection and checking out books and liner notes. Frank Sinatra's name came up in our conversation. We were talking about Ron Della Chiesa and how he was shifting from *Music America* to a weekly tribute radio program featuring Old Blue Eyes and his music. I told Charley that my favorite Sinatra album is *Sinatra at the Sands* with the Count Basie Band. Charley chimed in that he was the Count's band boy for that gig.

"You mean to say you were at the Sands that night?"

"Oh yes I was; it was a gala event celebrating Frank's fiftieth birthday. I was always an arm's length away from Basie, caring for all his needs, both good and bad."

I slept upstairs in the guest room, where John slept, in his bed. Rolled around all night, feeling eerie and uneasy, waiting for something. With certainty, it was a sleepless night for so many Dizzy lovers, filled with sadness and myriad thoughts.

In the morning over coffee, I said to Charley, "Ya know what's odd, but entirely true? For the eight years I've known John, there truly is not a bad thing I can say about him. I mean, you can't call a guy bad cuz he has a lot of gas. And when he did get his dander up, it was deserving, cuz what pissed him off was bad, genuinely bad, deservingly bad. Other than that, everything about him was so freaking good."

We picked up Ginny in Woonsocket and the three of us drove to John's funeral.

John had two funerals. The first one a private Bahá'í service for family and close friends. The second was held on 1/12/93 at the Cathedral of St. John the Divine on 110th and Amsterdam in New York City. St John's is a magnificent edifice, the fourth largest Christian church in the world, that was in a state of reconstruction due to a fire. It was the first time I met any of John's family other than Lorraine. There were over 10,000 people in attendance with an overflow of Dizzy admirers standing outside of the church. A tremendously diversified crowd of dignitaries to commoners, from all walks of life, all races and persuasions. I could just picture John, smiling, laughing, pointing that shaker stick at different characters.

Mayor David Dinkins gave a eulogy, as did Judge James Nelson, a leader of the Bahá'í faith. British pianist extraordinaire George Shearing told us a hilarious Dizzy tale, and Cab Calloway's daughter referred to John as "Uncle Dizzy." President-elect Bill Clinton sent a letter that was read by Thelonious Monk Jr. I sat next to Roberta Flack; at one point while music was playing, we hugged and kissed. That was a five-star kiss, baby. A musical procession made up of great musicians, primarily trumpeters, so many it's hard to remember them all, played and paraded through the church at service end. It was sad and magnificent. I've always felt the greatest Saint of all was the John being eulogized that very day.

Photo courtesy of the Charles Lake Collection.

The Whale's favorite star.

Aftermath

About three months after the funeral, during a severe Boston blizzard, Charley invited me to attend a Bahá'í gathering in South Boston. It was friendly and down-to-earth. The group was so pleased and couldn't get enough Dizzyana. They gingerly tried but couldn't get a couple of heathens like the Whale and me to sign up, which reminded me that Dizzy once said, "There's God, and then there's Duke Ellington."

Photo courtesy of the Charles Lake Collection.
Dizzy and Charles Moody burning at Newport Jazz Festival.

Five Year Anniversary Bash
Englewood, NJ

I attended a fifth year anniversary event sponsored by the Englewood (NJ) Hospital, where John was a patient during his bout with cancer. This was a bitter/sweet drive from Rhode Island to New Jersey. So many memories, myriads of moments, coursed through my mind, while I traveled along Interstate 95, up and onto the George Washington Bridge and into Englewood. While listening to CDs of John's music, I could picture him hugging Uncle Harry, those two nights at the Blue Note, tonk times, John's laugh, the falsetto stuttering, his love, his genius... The hospital set up a foundation in Dizzy's name dedicated to caring for indigent musicians. It was an enormous musical event, teeming with jazz legends. Unfortunately, Charley could not attend; however, Lalo Schifrin was there and, after the program, I told him about the night in Cambridge when, out of the blue in the middle of the night while playing tonk, John put his cards on the table and said, "I miss Lalo." Mr. Schifrin was speechless and tears just poured from his eyes. He simply said, "So special."

Ron Della Chiesa & Charley Lake Tel/Cons
March 27, 2014, 12:15 AK Time

I just got off the phone with Ron Della Chiesa and his wife, Joyce. They were mobile, heading towards Cape Cod for dinner. Ron and I have remained friends since his birthday bash at the Copley Plaza back in 1985. At a later date, I had the good fortune to visit him in Cambridge and sit in on his radio show, *Music America*. We had so much fun talking jazz and the wonderments of Dizzy. His book, *Radio My Way*, is like a musical encyclopedia. Besides several precious personal stories, I think of *Radio My Way* as one hundred fascinating biographies.

Ron D. understands the art of communicating, has a voice perfect for radio, a down to earth style, and a natural talent at conducting interviews. That style tends to influence and relax his guests. He let's people speak and asks great questions, which is what interviewers are suppose to do. Dizzy's *Music America* interviews with Ron are priceless. They should be released to the world. Those conversations went everywhere and anywhere, but always landed on their feet.

I asked Ron if he'd relate some stories about John. "I can do that. Give me a few days; I want to think on it." Ron also said, "Ya know, the Whale is making a great recovery. And he likes dialogue. You want his telephone number?"

As soon as I hung up with Ron, I dialed the Whale.

I knew Charley had a few health problems. About five years ago, I tried writing and calling him, with no response. So, it had been almost eight years since we last saw each other at a jazz club in Fort Lauderdale, where Charley had booked Scott Hamilton. The phone rang several times; I expected a voice asking to leave a message, when I heard a weak "Hello." No doubt, it was the Whale.

I said, "This is David G. Brown calling. I'd like to talk to Mr. Charles 'The Whale' Lake Keljakian ... please."

There was a pause, and he finally replied, "Do I owe you money?"

It was wonderful hearing that voice again. He sounded as though he had been through a few challenging rodeos, at 86 a tad slower on the draw, but surely on his game; a wit that was always at work. I asked him if he'd lay some Birks stories on me and he said that might not be so easy, "cuz they're all locked up and stored in my brain." I could respect and understand that. So, I said to him, "If you want to share anything with me, just call."

I couldn't resist and called Charley the next day. He initiated the conversation by asking, "Did you ever hear the name David Usher, David?"

"Can't say I have."

"He's from Detroit, deals in marine hazardous waste, and is a good friend of Dizzy."

"What are you getting at?"

"He just wrote a book, *Music is Forever, Dizzy Gillespie the Jazz Legend and Me.*"

"Did you read it?"

"I don't read," Charley replied. "Don't got the patience, but I know you read and write so I thought you might be interested."

"Thanks for the information, Charley." I paused and asked, "So what is it with jazz?"

"Whatdaya mean?"

"The draw. Why are we so caught up in this specific sound; this infection, affection, this jazz love affair. From whence does it come, Sire Charles?"

"Whatya takin a philosophy course, or somethin?"

"Nope. Just lookin for your take."

"Hm, hm, well, let's see. I'm from Chelsea, ya know. If you weren't cool in Chelsea, you'd get the shit kicked outta ya, see what I'm sayin. Like some cats didn't think Armenians are very cool. But playing the trumpet, like I did, was cool. And helpful. I learned by listening to the great jazz players; and the more I got interested, the more I fell for jazz."

"Hell of a start."

"Horns do it for me. Don't get me wrong, rhythm sections are beautiful, as well as strings. But, give me a horn player and I'm hooked. They lead the charge. They're a vision. What looks grander than a baritone saxophonist, a bari. How bout Gerry Mulligan up front with that tarnished, beatup repo he picked up at a hock shop in Minnesota. Miles all bent over doing cool. Then again, nothin compares to Birks, The Leader, godly I'm tellin ya; a vision to behold. Yup."

The Whale took a breath. "Jazz, great jazz ain't easy ya know. The way these guys play, at times I think it's a miracle. They are the coolest. Cerebral, quick on their feet, livin on the edge, witty beyond belief. Vulnerable."

"Vulnerable?"

"Of course, look around, look how many great musicians passed away before their time. To what? Temptation. These guys get done workin their ass off at one, two o'clock in the morning, all fired up, and someone suggests a drink, and the drink turns into some other cockamamie shit. It's sad, I'm tellin ya, very vulnerable."

We continued chatting about grass and drugs and the fact that neither of us, not once, ever saw John drink booze or do anything other than smoke pot.

"He was perfectly satisfied with ganja. Didn't hanker for anything else," Charley said. "Crazy that many of them cats didn't adhere to his standards. I guess it's just the nature of the beast."

We then switched conversation to the Bahá'ís. Charley said, "So many times we'd get off a plane and there'd be a cluster of them hanging around, looking for Birks. Very unobtrusive. And Birks always made a point of going over and talking to them."

"Yes. I can vividly picture a group of Bahá'ís hanging in front of the stage at the Newport Jazz Festival.

Very low key. And John spent plenty of time talking to those kind folks after his set. I paused. "There's a Bahá'í Center in Anchorage."

"Pay them a visit. Mention your link to Dizzy. He loved being Bahá'í. Everyone welcome."

We talked about preparing this book, and I said to him, "Ya know Sir Charles, let me reiterate; if you have any suggestions or ideas, call me. My cell phone is by my side. I don't sleep, man, I take naps."

"Neither do I." I could envision his smile through the phone. He said, "That's our breed. On the go all day. Two-five-slash-seven. But, getting back to your question, it's the musicianship, the speed and spontaneity. The variations. Take "Tunisia" for example. That song is amazing. It gives each musician an opportunity to show his stuff, her stuff. "Tunisia" is everything. Bebop art.

"So, I'm totally down. Jazz is the way I roll. I'm happiest and most comfortable when I can see it, hear it, smell it, you name it. It's jazz for me and anyone like me. Does that answer your question?"

Photo courtesy of the Charles Lake Collection.
Horn man and Whaler wall wailing.

"Like a Letter from Home"

Nice '89

Photo courtesy of the Charles Lake Collection.

The Whale said, "Many times Birks would buy a watermelon and hand it to the flight attendant when boarding a plane. He'd say, 'This is a letter from home; cut it up and share it.' Messages, Birks was always sending messages."

Thinking Out Loud

Some jazz connoisseur out there may be thinking, "Who the hell does this Brown guy think he is, writing about Dizzy Gillespie? He doesn't play an instrument, hasn't gone thru the drill of scale, cannot read music. He hasn't felt the rush of standing on a stage set in front of thousands and what it takes to deliver the goods. He don't know shit."

I sure have thought about that one. There's only one answer: Fate. Even John suggested that. It was good and delicious fate that united us in the second floor men's room at Blues Alley. Amen.

Mostly, I got to spend time with John during his off hours, when he lowered the shield and shared the scopes of his existence, from youth and the music, to growth and the journey. He explained his concerns, and loved to describe his tribulations. He had the answers and walked the walk. We talked some serious business in the wee small hours while dealing a deck of cards. I'm grateful for the knowledge and education. I've been with him in nine different states (FL, NY, NJ, RI, MA, VT, NH, CT, and VA) and the District of Columbia, but the best state of all is our bonded state of mind. When I'm not with him, I wish I were.

Diz & the Weins

FINIS - Dizzy Trip #3

Photo courtesy of the Charles Lake Collection.
Music producer George Wein admiring a Dizzy riff close up and personal at a private affair.

Tel/Con with Ron Della Chiesa
4/4/14

"Whenever I did an interview with Dizzy, it was a happening – a party broke out. The entire gang at WGBH would be waiting for him. He talked to everyone; people would come out of their offices and chat, ask for autographs, take photos. He was a born ham and loved to blow up those cheeks. Always took him a half hour to walk through the corridor and get to my studio.

"Finally, we'd settle in for the interview, and Charley Lake would open a paper bag with sandwiches, hummus and chips; then came dessert – all kinds of fruit. If you listened closely, you'd hear Dizzy chomping away. I only wish I could press a button and we could listen to some of those exchanges. By the way, Charley was a numerologist, you know; he'd stand in the back of the room, working numbers.

"The first time I saw Dizzy Gillespie play was at Boston's Symphony Hall in 1956. It was a Norman Granz event. Mr. Granz was a true jazz impresario – you know – going back to the late 40s. A great friend to so many jazz greats. He did not tolerate racism, and if he sensed it at a venue, he'd flat cancel the gig. Imagine, that was 58 years ago and it seems like yesterday. 'Jazz at the Philharmonic' productions – JATP. Granz held these at venues across the country. Some of the artists that night included Lester 'Prez' Young and Illinois Jacquet on tenor; Herb Ellis on guitar; Ray Brown, bass; Buddy Rich, the drummer; Oscar Peterson on piano; and trumpeter Roy Eldridge. Talk about a stacked lineup. They played a long rendition of 'How High's the Moon,' which is considered the national anthem of bebop.

"When Dizzy finally walked onstage, I was surprised to see the bell of his trumpet turned up 45 degrees. What the hell is that? I think I've mentioned to you I played trumpet back in the day. Never saw anything like that before. Of course, it became his trademark. He played a beautiful solo of 'I Can't Get Started'; then Roy Eldridge joined him and they got into a trumpet duel. A duel, like in the movie *High Noon*. Granz liked to do that; often times he'd have Buddy Rich and Louie Belson do a battle of the drums. Pretty cool, if you ask me. What I'll always remember about that night was the fire power coming out of Dizzy's horn. I was sitting in the second row. At one point I noticed when breath poured into his horn, then shot out the bell, I could see vapor. He was producing 'Dizzy steam.' He was on fire. That scene is burned into my memory.

"Dizzy had great admiration for Roy Eldridge, and Roy kind of acted as a bridge between Louis Armstrong and Dizzy. In other words, Satchmo got the first major recognition as a jazz trumpet, Roy sped up the process, then Dizzy brought the instrument and the sound to its watermark."

I asked Ron if he has Gillespie favorites?

"Oh yes, of course; but I think in terms of albums, not individual songs. My favorite is *Dizzy and Strings,* arranged and conducted by Johnny Richards. Remember, I'm a classical buff first and foremost. There are over 25 musicians on this album, including Quincy Jones, J. J. Johnson and Percy Heath. I just love the way it flows. And, I feel the same way about *Dizz and Roy,* recorded in 1954 in New York with Roy Eldridge, Oscar Peterson on piano, Ray Brown on bass, and drummer Louis Belson. This album makes you understand why Dizzy and Roy were so special, ahead of their times.

"Then, there's the Dizzy and Bird [Charlie Parker] album *Jazz at Massey Hall,* recorded in Toronto. Actually, this could be my favorite. Your question is too hard; all of these are number one favorites. For many, *Massey Hall* is the greatest bebop album ever recorded with Bird, Max Roach on drums, Bud Powell on piano, and bassist Charles Mingus. Back then they were called 'The Quintet.' Charlie Parker is listed as Charlie Chan on that album. It's the last recording of Dizzy and Bird playing together, and Mingus produced it. That same night was the Rocky Marciano / Jersey Joe Walcott heavyweight championship fight, which was shown on closed circuit at arenas across North America. Attendance was so poor for the gig that no one was paid. Can you imagine?"

There was a pause from my phone in Alaska to

Ron's ear in Massachusetts. I know we were both thinking that music lovers should have listened to *Massey Hall.* "What else should we talk about, Ron?"

"You know, when it comes to Dizzy, the stories are power-packed and never boring. Like his times in Cuba, smoking cigars with Fidel, which, by the way, didn't take too well with some patriots. His travels to the Middle East, playing for sheiks and his connection with the Bahá'í faith. Bringing his Big Band to the Newport Jazz Festival, I think in 56, maybe 57. A tremendous exhibition of musicianship, that also featured Dizzy's talent as a conductor.

"He was a freedom fighter, a marcher, was almost lynched down south; his mock run for president... What else can I say? There's no end to Dizzy stories... Yes, one more thought: I'd surely be remiss if I didn't tell you I expect that one hundred years from now, even two hundred years from now, time immemorial, Dizzy Gillespie's name will be revered and studied like Mozart and Beethoven."

Photo courtesy of the Charles Lake Collection. While producing *A Night in Havana,* Dizzy had cigar-smoking sessions with Fidel. They traded hats. At first glance it appears the Cuban leader might be pregnant. But no, it's a bullet-proof vest. He had to be sweating bullets in that thing.

Photo courtesy of William P. Gottlieb/Ira and Leonore S. Gershwin Fund Collection, Music Division, Library of Congress. LC-GLB23- 0284

Dizzy adored Ella. Both would be celebrating their 100th birthday in 2017 along with fellow jazz legends, Thelonious Monk and Buddy Rich. In my research, I've developed a revered link with journalist/photographer William P. Gottlieb, a true jazz impresario. It would have been an honor and joy to have walked the 52nd Street beat as his sidekick. RIP William Gottlieb (1917-2006).

This Shadow's Journey as a Jazz Raconteur

"One good thing about music, when it hits you, you feel no pain."
Bob Marley *(Trenchtown Rock)*

There was always sound blaring away from our duplex apartment on Meadow Road in Woonsocket. Our floor model Zenith radio framed in wood with all the mysterious bulbs in the back was set in a corner of the sunroom, and seemed to resonate throughout the whole neighborhood. My maternal grandmother referred to it as "that sound machine." Often times she'd sit attentively and in awe, asking anyone who'd listen, "How can sound come out of a wooden box?"

During those pre-TV years, Mr. Zenith evoked every emotion imaginable from tears to laughter, as we sat fixed in time, listening to presidential speeches, wartime news, Walter Winchell's dramatic reports, weather reports, and voting results.

Then there was the heavy-duty stuff – Red Sox baseball, especially those agonizing contests played against the rival NY Wankees, epic boxing matches (try closing your eyes and picturing Joe Louis knocking out Max Schmeling), and local Brown University football. We sat around that machine licking ice cream cones from Tate's Variety store and tuned in to awesome radio programs like *The Jack Benny Show,*

Phil Harris and Alice Faye, *The Shadow, I Love Luigi,* and *The Lone Ranger* with his kimosabi, Tonto.

And, of course, there was music. During his youth my father played the violin so he was naturally drawn to classical. He adored Itzhak Pearlman and was fascinated with Glenn Gould. He thought Al Jolson was god, Frank Sinatra was a "fish peddler," that Arturo Toscanini was the next coming, and Robert Merrill was the next, next coming. Every New Year's Eve, we heard Guy Lombardo and his Royal Canadians play *Auld Lang Syne* from the Hotel Roosevelt. Dad would always string along and say, "Now that's music." Personally, I thought Dad's greatest musical contribution was how he could slap Mr. Zenith just right to get rid of the static at the most critical moments.

My live music introduction occurred at the old Rhode Island Auditorium on North Main Street in Providence. Mom and Dad brought my brother and me out for an evening of entertainment to see the Spike Jones Orchestra. We had dinner across the street from the Auditorium at Tops Gaylord, a popular Rhode Island diner. When the menu was delivered, Mom elbowed me and said, "Don't go buyin the shrimp cocktail."

Now, I could tell Spike Jones was not quite Dad's cup of tea. He was tall, gangly and awkward, and didn't seem to play music seriously. Actually, that was his schtick. The guy was a musical comedian, more slapstick and less sophisticated than Victor Borge, and had the audience roaring with laughter. Even Dad loosened up by show's end. Most importantly, anyone watching closely could tell that it took a terrific effort from all of Spike's musicians to perform with excellence. I walked away from that concert in love with both watching and listening to music. Never learned to play an instrument; but, from that day forth, I gained the highest regard for all musicians.

I had a momentary glimpse of live jazz at the age of thirteen in 1954. It was on a weekend holiday in New York City. We stayed at the Roosevelt Hotel (no Guy Lombardo sightings). On Saturday, my parents joined my Uncle Harry for a baseball game at Yankee Stadium. And my nineteen-year-old brother and I were left to fend for ourselves. We boogied out of the Roosevelt like Usain Bolt. Went to the automat, Empire State Building, Statue of Liberty; rode the subway; and in the evening, we roamed Broadway. At one point, we came upon a nightclub called the Metronome. Walked right in and was face-to-face with Lionel Hampton. Had never seen a vibraphone in my life. Could not believe how fast his hands moved; and watching those percussion mallets dancing up and down in a blur was magic. We only lasted a few minutes before the host shooed us away. No minors allowed.

Slipping into my teens, I never particularly cared for rock and roll music. Will admit I did like rocking and rolling around the clock with Bill Haley and the Comets. And who wouldn't be taken by Elvis with his shiny-slick black hair, that sexy deep voice, and his look in uniform when he was inducted into the army. He was so loved by my fellow high schoolers. I did get a kick out of Little Richard (Richard Wayne Penniman), and Chuck Berry brought me to "Memphis Tennessee." Jerry Lee Lewis' piano was filled with fury, and Roy Orbison's voice had em all beat. Not sure how to perfectly express my take on rock and roll other than it was fun, but lacking. Forgive me.

It was the more mellow sounds that drew me in, works from the *Great American Songbook*. I adored the voices of Sinatra, Joe Williams, Louis "Satchmo" Armstrong, Tony Bennett, Ray Charles, and, Nat King Cole. Bought my first record album on a "layaway plan" at Music Box in downtown Woonsocket. Cost me $3.99; a green and grey cover featuring Harry Belafonte's *Mark Twain and Other Folk Favorites* (RCA Victor LPM1022). When I got my driver's license at age sixteen, my first major journey was to a nightclub in South Boston, Blinstrub's, to see Johnny Mathis. Even had a date. Johnny was divine.

One afternoon while driving through Randall Square in Providence, my brother pulled into the parking lot of the Celebrity Club. This would be 1955, during the youth of my jazz love affair. I ran inside just to take a look. The place was empty except for a floor sweeper and a faint smell of booze and cigarettes. What I remember was a long rectangular stage. All I could do was imagine the great players who stood on that floor. Randall Square is the equivalent of Scollay Square in Boston. Both tough sections of town. Scollay was filled with Irish pubs and noted for it's burlesque shows that featured all kinds of music and scantily clad female dancers. Randall Square was a hangout for toughs, and jazz at the Celebrity Club. Neither exist today; Scollay is now an extension of Boston's north end and Randall is filled with stores and medical buildings. They are like the ever-changing structures of rivers and streams.

My brother had a friend from Providence, Marvin "Butch" Hodosh, and one evening at Butch's home, he showed me his records. They filled an entire bookcase along a wall in his bedroom. All jazz albums with stunning covers and liner notes. Butch, acting just like a disc jockey, played his favorites – Maynard Ferguson, Ellington, The Count, Bird and Yard, Jean-Baptiste "Illinois" Jacquet, and Erroll Garner, who hummed and grunted while playing piano. Then he spun Billie Holiday. Oh my. The soul in her voice took me to a smokey place. Then Ella Fitzgerald. I asked Butch, "What's she doing?" "That's scat." He told me about the Newport Jazz Festival, which he attended that summer (1956), and a performance of the ages by Duke Ellington and his band. He said a saxophonist by the name of Paul Gonzalves from Brockton got up and played a 27-chorus solo in the middle of Ellington's "Diminuendo and Crescendo in Blue." "The place went nuts; there was almost a riot." I sat captivated in envy that I wasn't there. His last piece – and a song that is on my top ten list – was "A Night in Tunisia" by Dizzy Gillespie. Those high notes. Charlie Parker wailing on alto. Butch looked at me knowingly. "What you just heard is monumental shit." I left Butch's place out of my vertigoed mind, void of compass, with no sense of direction other than the certainty that jazz was to become my favorite musical genre.

After graduating high school and working in one of Woonsocket's textile factories, I picked up my buddy Stevie Max in Pawtucket and drove to Newport for the 1958 Jazz Festival. Stevie was my #2 mentor after Butch. Marijuana was not around then, at least not for us, but we did have a cooler full of beer. What a lineup of all-stars I would see that weekend, including Miles, The Duke, Mahalia Jackson, Thelonius Monk, John Coltrane, Anita O'Day, Dave Brubeck, Dinah Washington, Sonny Stitt and a lady by the name of Big Maybelle... Suffice to say it was one of the greatest collection of jazz artists ... eva, ever, I'm tellin ya.

Sad to say I was on my way back to Woonsocket on Saturday night due to sunstroke. What happened, you ask? After the Friday night program, we drove over to Second Beach to sack out. There were bongo drummers banging away all night and it was impossible to sleep. By sunrise the percussion ceased and I finally passed out; for eight hours laying in the sand, rolling over, one shoe missing, and a body that looked like it had been rolling in a rotisserie for a month. So I missed some major sets of music. But I did see an amazing Friday night, sitting in an audience filled with Newport's rich and famous and kids like myself. I was taken by the size of Jimmy Rushing, both his height and overpowering voice.

George Wein pulled an offbeat surprise by closing that Friday night with rock-and-roller Chuck Berry. It was different and a break from tradition. The crowd seemed to swell and everything became more animated. Standing in the shadows of Freebody Park that July 4th night was suspended euphoria. Chuck Berry burned. There was so much screaming, so much joy. Such music. Black night, black artist, black audience. It was a game-changer for me regarding my evolution and understanding(s) of people, and life itself.

Wein broke tradition on more than one occasion. One year in the early nineties, he had Isaac Hayes close the show, and on another, Stevie Ray Vaughn did the same. Never even heard of Stevie Ray. Now, he's my Texas bluesman, pride and joy.

Paul Waldman, a longtime friend from Providence, and I attended a camp in Amesbury, MA, for several years – Camp Bauercrest. It was near the New Hampshire border and often times we'd sneak off to Salisbury Beach, which had an amusement park set right off the sand and surf, so close you could hear the roar of the waves. There was a music venue at Salisbury called the Frolics and they brought in top entertainment. Can remember standing behind that building, chomping on a slice of pizza and faintly hearing Sammy Davis Jr. perform. Oh my, how I loved his music.

Shuffle forward several years. Both Paul and I were going to school in Boston. It was February 9, 1962, my 21st birthday, and we returned to Blinstrub's to catch Sammy Davis Jr. and the Will Mastin Trio. What a night; great seats, excitement and electricity filled the room. Sammy did everything – sing, dance, play instruments, tell jokes, and do imitations. So good we went back two more nights. In my opinion, Sammy is the greatest entertainer that ever lived. There was nothing he couldn't do musically except leave the stage. He once said, "If I open the refrigerator in the middle of the night, as soon as the light goes on, I perform for twenty minutes."

My record collection grew by leaps and bounds, as did my life. Love and marriage, kids, long hours working in our family business, continued education for all of us, ballgames, growing pains and bill-paying.

Thankfully, music was always there. Woonsocket compadres John Chan, Dennis McKenna, Paul Staiti and I would catch jazz events whenever we could – Mel Tormé at Veterans Memorial Auditorium in downcity Providence, Scott Hamilton and Warren Vaché at the El Morocco in Worcester, Kinky Freedman and the Texas Jewboys in NYC. We even flew down to Philadelphia to spend time with Leon Redbone and celebrate his tuba player's birthday. That would be the dapper Jonathan Dorn. We had an amazing dinner at The Victor Café in South Philly. There was a sign that said if you dared to stand up and sing a song, and got a standing ovation, dinner was on the house. Still disappointed that Redbone didn't take on the challenge.

Photo by John Chan.
Leon Redbone and author at Victor's Cafe in So. Philly.

It's worth mentioning that during that period I became friendly with Drew Palmer, owner of *The Woonsocket Call*. He gave me a press pass with a photo and I started freelance writing. That laminated ID got me into a lot of places for sporting events and musical concerts. Wrote a few articles for *The Call*. The best part was interviewing Jerry Lee Lewis and Sammy Davis Jr. at the old Warwick Musical Tent.

Speaking of Rhode Island venues, it was in the early 80s when I discovered Monday nights at Bovi's in East Providence. My first visit was with John Chan and I loved the seventeen piece resident band led by Duke Belaire. That night, Duke invited Rose Weaver to sing a few songs. Rose is quite the gal; an accomplished singer and thespian, who has performed on both coasts and has starred in a number of programs at the Trinity Repertory Company in Providence including *A Christmas Carol* and *Lady Day Sings the Blues* (Rose transformed into Billy Holiday). And it was Rose who later suggested, maybe I'd be interested in becoming a music agent. I did, and for about ten years booked mostly jazz and reggae. My very first gig featured Rose and the Greg Wardson Trio along with Greg Abate and his Channel One Band at Congregation B'nai Israel in Woonsocket. My most illustrious event was held in Newport at the above mentioned Goat Island Sheridan, where Dizzy played with the quintet. Earlier that evening Greg Abate performed and I sat with Ron Halloway, who thought Greg played an excellent horn.

Photo by author.
Ron Halloway at Goat Island Sheridan.

I have encores of admiration for Greg Abate. He played sax for the Woonsocket High School Band, graduated from Boston's Berklee College, played sax in the Ray Charles Band and the Artie Shaw Band, and lead sax for the Duke Belaire Band, where he demonstrated his skills on all the saxophones and flute. He has also led several groups of his own over the last forty years and was recently inducted into the Rhode Island Music Hall of Fame.

Greg has a Dick Johnson face, one that looks like he was born to blow a horn.

John Chan introduced me to Greg in 1981 and our friendship lingers. We've invented our own language and continuously text back and forth building toward a crescendo with our co-authored science fiction thrilla about the legend of Armando Armandillio. That's the serious side of our palship.

During those early years on Thursday nights, I would drive into Providence to watch Greg play with his Channel One Band at Allary's on North Main Street. They did mostly fusion and Greg would, and still does, burn up the room. Those were late night/ early morning sessions filled with laughs as well as serious dialogue ranging from politics to music, and his latest arrangement of "Al di lá."

Helped finance Channel One's first album, *Without Boundaries,* at Normandy Sound in Warren, RI. Paul Murphy, the band's lead guitar and ad hoc financier, never missed a payment until my loan was paid off. RIP Paul.

It's been bitter/sweet watching Greg grow over the years in jazz. A slow grind, sometimes humbling, especially having to handle the bulk of the promo work along with bookings, and failed expectations. But, to his credit, Greg has gained recognition to the point he's now traveling internationally with a full schedule. His latest album, *Kindred Spirits, Live at Chan's* (Whaling City Sound WCS 077), features Phil Woods. It was Phil's last recording and has gotten excellent reviews.

Greg has been a wonderful muse for a music romanticist and ear like myself. His sharing and taking me to classes at Rhode Island College where he teaches has given me a chance to learn some of the technicalities of playing his instruments. I feel just a tad more intimate at a performance than the average Joe.

Photo by David Arruda Jr., Courtesy of Whaling City Sound.
Greg Abate's latest album with the late Phil Woods.

I must share a story about Red Lennox, a school teacher, mind you, from the Woonsocket suburb of Cumberland, RI, and a trumpet player at Bovi's. Red stood in Duke Belaire's back row/left for decades.

He was close friends with Dave McKenna and one night I ran into them at the Copley Plaza. After a few drinks, Red elbowed me. "Hey, let's take a walk and smoke some of my weed." "But there's no place to do this." Undeterred, he confidently replied, "Follow me." So, we slipped into an elevator and got off at one of the upper floors, found a corner, and Red instantly lit up his pipe. No sooner did Red extinguish his instrument of euphoria when we heard the elevator door open and people – fast moving people, security types – were advancing in our direction. I was wearing a suit and tie and Red was looking dapperly dope, so we walked right towards them. One asked, "Are you the gentlemen who called?" "Yes," Red replied. "Something smells back there, something ain't right." And we kept walking with a shit-eating grin on our faces. Never looked back. We coulda gotten arrested, for cryin out loud. Now reefer is legal in Massachusetts. Red Lennox, mean horn.

Meanwhile, John Chan started holding musical events at his family restaurant in Woonsocket. And his venue has turned into a New England hot spot for quality music with very respectful and appreciative audiences. Cudos to the Chanman.

Photo by John Chan.

Great schedule.

Rhode Island can be proud of it's jazz heritage. This is not a full slate, but pianist Dave McKenna; vocalist and pianist Daryl Sherman; Clay Osborn; tenor Scott Hamilton; saxmen Art Pelosi, Ed "The Zman" Zeresky and Harry Allen; Rose Weaver; and Greg Abate are worthy starters.

So many marvelous artists and events; so many great times and conversations. Here are some cameos of jazz adventures I've experienced over the years:

For two summers during my college years, I worked in a resort hotel in New Hampshire and became friends with Joel Smith from the Bronx and Bruce Krell from Miami Beach. We had a reunion in the Big Apple and, on Saturday night, got seats for Ella Fitzgerald at the Village Vanguard. We didn't have enough money to pay the tab.

Spending an evening with Dakota Staton at the Howard Johnson's on Beacon Street in Boston. This was during the latter part of her singing career. After her late, late show and back in her room, she wore sweat pants, munched on chocolate bonbons, and called me "Honey." Dakota became my third grand-mother.

The Whale took me to Brown University, where he booked the vibraphonist, Terry Gibbs, a short in stature man who is filled with wit and a whirling dervish with his mallets. Sat in awe just like I did watching Lionel Hampton at the Metronome decades earlier. What a visual instrument. Then we were off to Bovi's in East Providence to see Albuquerque's Bobby Shew play trumpet with the John Allmark Band.

At Seattle's most noted jazz venue, Demetriou's, a few blocks from the Space Needle, I spotted pianist McCoy Tyner sitting at a table by himself drinking soup. After two sets, he looked small, bent, and tired. With reservation I walked over to share a few words. He did look lonely, and maybe I shouldn't have dis-turbed him, but I was curious and couldn't resist. Turns out he was pleased to have company. His voice was deep and husky; sounded like a character from *Goodfellas.*

Interviewed Sarah Vaughn after her session at the Newport Jazz Festival. She told me about waking up that morning with food poisoning from dinner at a Newport restaurant the night before. Her performance was one for the ages.

Upstairs in the dressing room at the Blue Note, I asked Claudio Roditi a stupid question: "What are you trying to do?" And he replied, "I want every note to be one of consequence." To this day it's one of my favorite lines.

John Chan and I saw Leon Redbone open for George Carlin at Veterans Memorial Auditorium near the statehouse in Providence, RI. Although Redbone could best be described as a Django Reinhardt bluesman, he's one jazzy bon vivant. After the show we all drove back to Chan's to feast in the Vault Room (the restaurant used to be a bank!). Carlin wanted us to tell jokes and funny experiences. He said, "That's how I get a lot of my material."

I lived in the San Francisco area on several different occasions. Didn't take long to become my favorite city. Spent a night at the famous Fillmore watching and listening to Black Uhuru. Reggae, not jazz, but they could fit if called upon. Tremendous percussive sounds. Uhuru bleeds the black, green, and yellow of the Jamaican flag.

My first Arturo Sandoval experience occurred at the Boston Opera House. As previously mentioned, he played that night with Dizzy's United Nations Band. I also saw him at Yoshi's in Oakland and the San Francisco Jazz Club. Yoshi's is one of the world's finest jazz rooms and the SF Jazz Club is a close second. Neither are smoke-filled, boozy juke joints. They are acoustically sound with a sterile and modern ambiance. Sandoval sang and played five different instruments. I do believe he's today's greatest trumpet in the world. I know that's debatable. Call me and we can argue. The two Arturo's, Toscanini and Sandoval.

Sad to report that Pearl's on Columbus Avenue closed down a few years ago. It was just below the intersection of Broadway where the Hungry Eye used to be, and is now a strip club. It was located near my favorite Italian restaurant, Marconi's. Sure do miss Pearl's. Rendezvoused there with Greg Abate and saw a brilliant drummer, Babatunde Lea. Drove up to Vallejo to watch Babatunde's quartet play in a small room, the Poetry and Jazz Club. They were wonderful. A dude, I think the owner, sporting a tall afro got up and read some heavy poetry between sets.

Back to Rhode Island. Let me pull a George Wein and sidestep from the world of jazz for a moment to share an evening I spent at Meehan Auditorium on the Brown University campus. It was the autumn of 1981 and Jamaican poet/prophet Bob Marley along with the Wailers and the I Threes performed. There was enough ganja flowin tru the air in that hockey arena to get all of Providence stoned. This would be on Robert Nesta's last tour after he had been diagnosed with cancer. It was an amazing event. The way the soundman danced was worth the price of admission. We all sat fixated in our seats as this group of amazing artists presented the best of reggae music, which included several jazz riffs. With his boundless energy and long dreads flowing, Bob sang, worked his guitar, and danced through most of his repertoire for over two hours.

Besides the above cameos, there was additional Dizzy-time. Mostly short-lived, no tonk, but nevertheless opportunities to be close and watch the maestro jump to the bar:

∽

Attended a ceremony at Berklee School of Music where Mr. Gillespie was awarded a Doctorate Degree. Lots of smiles throughout the room. And several students played their hearts out. All Dizzy compositions. My favorite was sung by this sweet little thing who sang and scatted through "Ooh Shoobie Doobie."

Photo courtesy of the Charles Lake Collection.
Dizzy receiving doctorate degree at Berklee College.

Photo by R. Ferrier.
Dizzy sitting with Lawrence Berklee after receiving
honorary Doctorate Degree at Berklee College of Music.

❧

Visited the Washington Museum of Art. Hell of a music venue. Only caught part of the gig, but John introduced me to Mr. Charles Fishman, Dr. Gillespie's general manager and producer of the DC Jazz Festival. Great sense of humor and he was wearing a yarmulke. We had a pleasant, but brief, conversation. I told him about my trip to Jamaica with hopes to set Dizzy up with Rita Marley and her musical posse. We never spoke again.

❧

During the day, I had attended an Independent Insurance Agents of New England conference. After dinner and several drinks, on a spur-of-the-moment whim, I jumped into a taxi and headed over to The Channel. This club, which features more rock and roll events than jazz, reminded me of Lupo's Heartbreak Hotel in Providence and the Fillmore in SF, where the audiences are usually sardine-packed and standing throughout the whole gig. Dizzy had John Faddis on-board along with the quintet. The crowd was mostly boozed-up or stoned college kids. The boys had to turn the volume up for this struggle. Shook John's hand after the gig. His eyes got big and he asked, "What the f--k are you doing here?" I replied, "What the fuck are you doing here?"

❧

I made arrangements with Charley to meet John, the quintet, and him at a hotel near Mystic,

Connecticut, one early summer evening. The plan was for all of us to drive in a limo from the hotel to an outdoor venue.

That day I played a round of golf and had several beverages afterwards. Dragged my buddy Ritchie Ruggerio along. It was a day of controlled chaos; I only say that because we somehow managed to find the hotel where, in quick order, we were shuffled into the limo and driven off into the woodlands of Connecticut. With these exchanges of vehicles (the limo had its own built-in bar, by the way, and there was a stack of joints sitting in a glass), this scenario felt more like a subversive drug deal or a mafia hit in motion. Most of the evening was vague. I remember sitting next to John, who was in marvelous spirits, and looking across at Ritchie and the Whale. Somewhere the quintet was squeezed on board and there was lots of commotion both coming and going. The performance was held in this lovely rustic park; not sure if it was public or private but it was as perfectly groomed as the golf course we played on earlier in the day. Recall nothing of the performance other than seeing the most beautiful flower beds of peonies, rose bushes and other varieties of aromatics. And there were countless rows of wooden seats, so many they seemed to disappear into a vortex of putting greens. All I know is we made it back to the hotel, no one was shot, I drove Ritchie home, and have survived to tell you about this momentous occasion. My guess is most readers could share a similar experience of their own.

Voila. That's a summary of what brought me to music, jazz and my favorite maestro. Please take note there is hardly any hostility or conflict in "Shadowing." These are normally requisites in most books. But, ya know, with the temper of today's times, filled with rancor, division, and falsehoods, I've tried to play a different trump card.

John Birks Dizzy Gillespie

"Up above my head, there's music in the air..."

Cheraw, South Carolina, described as "The Prettiest Town in Dixie," is also the home of Triumph The Church Kingdom of God, founded in 1924 by Elder J. E. Burch. Mr. Burch was a stately, well-groomed, versatile man, who owned a store, boarding house and restaurant. He was also a singer and preacher. His contributions to the Cheraw Black community were monumental, providing all the necessary social activities for a segregated family.

As fate would have it, John lived next door to the Triumph. He was born and blessed with the sounds of music flowing through his ears, through his entire being, as if the sounds of Jonah were wailing from heaven. On a daily basis, he'd hear the voices of gospel, Delta blues, and protest songs. The church was a constructive force built into his foundation. It was his introduction to rhythms and harmonies, society and reality. During those formative years John played music with several of Elder Burch's sons. (Re: PBS, "Blood and Soil")

Shortly after talking with Ron Della Chiesa and watching "Blood and Soil" in early June, it clearly occurred to me I shared another commonality with John. A nexus, a link, a strong connection that hit me like a Gillespian high note backed by countless harps and eternal cellos.

We both lived with the taste and torture of racism and antisemitism. John, a direct descendant of Black African slaves, while I listened to my family talk in tongues, in Yiddish, and suffer from the reports of atrocities spreading all over Europe. I learned the definition of Holocaust as a three-year-old in 1944.

We talked about this, John and I, late at night. Serious talks that brought sadness and pain. Stories about Blacks being beaten and Jews being burned. People that were actually related to us. Our conversations changed lanes from grief to disbelief ... then answers – better education, the golden rule, Bob Marley, what could be done to save the coming generations. We felt smart ... and then we'd smirk at reality – about what politricks was and is all about.

And I must assure you, we were optimists; swear to God. We always got back to the positive side, the sunny side, in spite of all the vampires and bullshit, giving thanks for all our good fortune, playing tonk with a full deck.

It was a hell of a bond. It pleases me; I get goosebumps visualizing his face, the broad frowns and his voice of sincerity. John Birks stood up. He defined pride. I have grand admiration and thoroughly enjoy sitting in his pew. Uh huh. He was a freedom fighter of public consequence; deeply concerned.

Fascinating, that over a period of time, John became

a member of the Bahá'í faith.

Dizzy worked smart. His musicians looked sharp. He was their imperial leader. His musical selections for every performance were well thought out. And when he took the lead, most everyone was on the edge of their seat. Like a freight train, he'd get rolling and build momentum. He'd put his right foot forward and point that bell skyward with the look of a charging bull, eyes bulging above his drawn-in lips and extended cheeks. Oh those cheeks, so fundamentally unsound, yet so magical.

Wish I could have been in New York in the 1940s in Harlem or on 52nd Street, at bistros like Minton's, the Onyx, the Three Deuces or the Cotton Club, where pomp, character, and smoky ambiance filled the air. Looking at old photos, I try to transcend into that era with visions of Dizzy as a confident bon vivant, rainbows shooting out of his bell, carousing and dancing with the stars.

Charlie Parker and Dizzy in action had to compare to a heavyweight championship fight. Every time they capitulated, those moments should have been recorded for posterity. Writers, and those who have a penchant for dialogue, would have reveled over words shared between those two. (Imagine a t-shirt or bumper sticker that reads "Dizzy Bird.")

Quotes from most of John's fellow musicians and friends from the early years all seem to echo the same theme. They smile and nod and imitate his throaty voice and the staccato stuttering. They speak with reverence. About music, they all unequivocally say he never held back, always willing to share.

After a superb performance at the San Francisco Jazz Club (December 2013), Arturo Sandoval said, "Dizzy Gillespie saved my ass. Without him, I'd probably still be in Cuba." Sandoval's latest album is dedicated to Dizzy and he sings "Every Day, I Think of You." It is so warm, heartfelt, and personal, you can feel Dizzy's presence.

There must be some folks out there that don't take kindly to John. It's said that during the late-hour Harlem jams, there were times he acted smug and superior to aspiring interlopers who were summarily turned away as lesser talents. As a leader he was a taskmaster, a perfectionist; and maybe he offended some who were less committed.

For most people, when they fathom an image of Dizzy Gillespie, they picture this stout, southern, comical hipster with cool threads and those blown-out cheeks, percolating sound from his famed up-tilted-bell trumpet. My first image of John is not physical. I fathom never-ending energy, "25/7" creativity, intelligence, supreme confidence and invulnerability. Then, I hear his infectious laugh and that deep voice. I love that voice. When thinking about John, I conjure up experiences I've had with him, how interesting he made everything always something memorable.

Compared to most, John led an enviable life. He did what he loved. Loved to travel; there were several years where he performed over 300 nights, having the time of his life, showing what he stood for, gaining tribulations. He loved to eat, often to be found at the finest restaurants, chomping away. His voracious expressions of gas said it all. He loved to tell stories, never ending. He functioned in all tenses.

One of the best lessons I learned from Professor Gillespie came in Burlington, VT, on that crazy night when John played dizzy and bounced the balloon all the way to the hotel. It was spontaneous and hilarious. To some it may have looked ridiculous. About that time, I had been working twenty-plus years, long and tedious hours. Business kept me up nights, anxiety and angst were setting in along with acid reflux and a hiatal hernia. And here we were like three silly kids. That stayed with me. It made me think, "What does John do? He plays music. He's a player." That doesn't mean he hasn't paid his dues; I still remember his words in Waterville Valley when he declared he's from the school of hard knocks. But, what do kids want the most – to have fun and be happy – to play. The pure truth is that we adults are all kids up till the very end. John refreshed my memory, reset my priorities, and changed my ways.

I feel his handshake and arms in a hug. I feel anointed that I've had the opportunity to spend the countless hours I did with him. Just incredible, every moment one of substance. He is a man who fired me up just by his presence, just thinking about being in his presence.

Been on the phone with the Whale a lot lately. "You know about Charles Fishman, don't you?" he asked.

"Yes, I do. You've mentioned him several times, and I chatted with him briefly at the Washington Art Museum. This had to be around 1989."

"Oh yeh. He's a pro producer."

"You've made that clear, Charley, and he acted as John's agent for a long time."

"That's right. Well, he's scheduling a 100th birthday bash for Birks at The Kennedy Center for the Arts in DC on October 21. I wanna go to that gig."

I could sense the urgency in Charley's voice. "And you will. Maybe Ron Della Chiesa will go with you. Shit, I'll fly down and we'll have a reunion."

"You'd do that?"

"Yes I would, sire."

"Wouldn't that be somethin." He paused. "It ain't a simple proposition. There seems to be a problem."

"What's the matter."

"Well, I've been trying to call him. Left a phone message. No reply. Ginny's been trying. He doesn't call back."

"Want me to try?"

"Sure, go ahead. Have him call me. He's a master of logistics and would always make flight and hotel arrangements for us. Always on the money. And he's the kind of guy that returns calls, immediately. So, I don't get it. I'd feel so much better if I could talk to him and know what's going on."

"We'll get to the bottom of this, Charley. Don't fret." It was disconcerting hearing the Whale's concern and I changed subjects.

"Charley, you been keeping an eye on the news lately?"

"Whatya mean?"

"I know John would not be pleased with our progress in politics."

"Progress you say?"

"I'm being satirical."

"I'm afraid this shit-show is no joke. What's goin on here since the 2016 election is totally contrary to Birks' convictions, what he stood for. He'd be pissed off, and so am I."

"I agree Charley, and I'm certain he'd be standing up and being heard."

"Yes he would. He'd be sendin out messages. This is serious business, brother."

BB King sings a song, "There Must Be A Better World Somewhere." BB says it all. As a matter of fact, most of the great musical artists like Dizzy, Leonard Cohen, Bob Marley and Bob Dylan all sing it like it is.

No sooner did I hang up the phone, Charley called me right back. He said with a choked up tone, "I forgot to tell you I drempt about him last night. We were walking on the beach in Revere. He used to call me 'Cut Man,' which he did, you know. I kept asking him, 'Where are we going?' He didn't answer. We just kept walking."

"No kidding. It happens to me too, Charley. Always good, never a nightmare, usually something funny goin on."

"That's right. I'm sure he's sending messages and keeping an eye on us." Charley hesitated. "God, I miss him."

"Yeh. Ya know, Whale..."

"What's that?"

"He woulda made an excellent president."

PS: Happy One-Hundredth Birthday, John. With Love.

THE END

Photo courtesy of the Charles Lake Collection.

Photo courtesy of the Charles Lake Collection.
"Let's consider options..."

Photo courtesy of the Charles Lake Collection.
The maestro performed on many cruise ships. On occasion he'd manage to
jump off board.

Acknowledgements

What a project. What fun. What a link to reality.

I spent six years researching and writing a true crime book, *Deacon's Crossbow,* about a friend of mine who killed a man with a crossbow. It was not fun – heartbreaking and sad. Of course there's some sadness and heartbreak in Dizzy's story. But, all the joy I experienced reliving John moments far out-weighed – and made up for – those six daunting years.

If John was writing these acknowledgments, I know he'd mention with high regard most every musician he played with, along with Ginny, Tony Bennett, Charley "The Whale" Lake and Ron "The Voice" Della Chiesa, John Dimitrio, Charles Kaufman, harmony grits, and Barack Obama.

For their love of music, jazz, and bebop, I care to acknowledge the following folk who helped shape my words: Cole, Madi and Barbara Brown; Paul Staiti; Jack Casey; Scott Minor; Jerry Rosenberg (Chair of the Photography Dept); Maureen Hanlon, my top critic; Velma and Marty Felder (Inspiration Dept); Rene Berard; John Chan of "ribs, wings and jazz" fame; my readers – especially Lori Townsend, the voice of Alaska Public Radio; and Kaya, my twenty-pound terrier, who faithfully sits by my side each day as I punch out paragraphs. Thank you my dear friends. You all make life so much more rewarding.

Then there's Johanna Bohoy of Bohoy Design. My

longtime Rhode Island pal Larry Berk is married to Johanna. He introduced us in the 80s and I've been marveling at her artistic abilities since. She did the cover for *Deacon's Crossbow* and I know Dizzy would love this cover.

And a final bow to mein pal, Bob Golden (my lovable half-empty cup of coffee). We go back to the 1940s. Bob was my neighbor and now my publisher, editor, and critic.

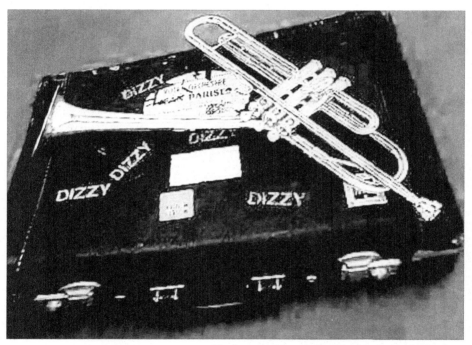

Photo courtesy of the Charles Lake Collection.

About the Author

Photo courtesy of Scott Minor Photography

David G. Brown grew up and worked in Woonsocket, RI. He is the father of two sons, has two grandchildren, and lives with his significant better half, Maureen Hanlon. An avid reader and writer, he credits the Creative Writing program at Cuesta College (CA) and the Alaska Writers Guild for advancing his writing career. Mr. Brown freelanced for *The Woonsocket Call, Castro Valley Forum* (CA), and *Edible East Bay* (CA). He is the author of a true crime book, *Deacon's Crossbow,* and his current writing project is an historical novel, *Return of the Free Faller.* Extra curricular activities include politricks (disliking it), sports (especially fishing), music, creative writing workshops, and spending as much time as possible with his dog, Kaya. He now resides in Anchorage, AK.

A true-crime thriller
by David G. Brown

How does a high school valedictorian, former member of the famed 101st Airborne, respected church deacon, husband and father of three end up with a first-degree murder conviction and serving life without parole?

Deacon's Crossbow: The True Story of a Crossbow Killing on Interstate 95 is a bone-chilling and compelling work of true crime about fate, fear, facts and personality, especially that of convict Donald S. Graham.

Donald and his wife were driving home from dance lessons when they happened upon two men on Interstate 95 in Massachusetts. When Donald reached for his crossbow, all hell broke loose. The end result: the male driver is dead and the deacon is in prison for the rest of his life. You'll follow a labyrinth of events from the incident all the way to the present. The story is unique because it includes Mr. Graham's views and sentiments from within the walls of incarceration, as well as perspectives from a free man, the author.

Was justice served? Was the driver the aggressor and the deacon the victim? You decide.

CPSIA information can be obtained
at www.ICGtesting.com
Printed in the USA
BVOW06s1922011117
499283BV00009B/242/P